GAME OF KNOWNS

Also by Dr Karl Kruszelnicki

Curious & Curiouser

Brain Food

50 Shades of Grey Matter

Dinosaurs Aren't Dead

Dr Karl's Big Book of Science Stuff and Nonsense

GAME OF KNOWNS

SCIENCE IS COMING...

DR KARL KRUSZELNICKI

MACMILLAN

First published 2013 in Macmillan by Pan Macmillan Australia Pty Ltd

1 Market Street, Sydney

Cataloguing-in-Publication entry is available

from the National Library of Australia

http://catalogue.nla.gov.au

Cover, internal design and typeset by Xou Creative, www.xou.com.au

Original cover photo of Dr Karl by David Stefanoff

Internal illustrations by Douglas Holgate

Printed by McPherson's Printing Group

This book is dedicated to the memory of Simon Newcomb (1835–1909), the self-taught mathematician and astronomer. In his stellar career, he rose to become Professor of Mathematics and Astronomer at the United States Naval Observatory and later Director of the US Nautical Almanac Office. He also did important work with Benford's Law (that in a list of numbers, more will begin with the digit "1" than with any other digit), the Speed of Light, and the Chandler Wobble (the 9-metre 14-month wobble of the Poles).

However, he did say in 1888, "Unfortunately, we are probably nearing the limit of all we can know about astronomy."

But being a true scientist, if he could see what we now know, he would be jumping for joy over the Moon, not turning in his grave.

CONTENTS

3D PRINTING

A few animals, such as apes and otters, use sticks and stones as tools. Even so, we humans classify ourselves as the Tool-Making Animal. Well, a little while ago we humans invented a new tool, and it seems it will revolutionise our manufacturing industries over the next few decades.

It can potentially make anything – a working clock, jewellery, vaccines, a metal axle for your car, toys, a tooth, a human organ, a violin, a hand gun, slightly different-sized shoes that fit your left and right feet perfectly, or a chain-mail vest with a zip down the back. It can even make an exact copy of itself.

3D PRINTER 101

This new tool is called, rather confusingly, a "3D Printer".

But it does not print 3D pictures, the kind that spring to life when you look at them with special glasses. No, it fabricates actual three-dimensional objects, one thin layer at a time – and then builds up hundreds or thousands of these layers on top of each other until the object is completed.

So why did the process get called "3D Printing"?

Well, one popular type of regular paper printer is the inkjet printer. It prints onto paper by squirting out tiny balls of ink from tiny nozzles. These balls of ink are so little that it would take thousands of trillions of them to make up a litre.

> A 3D printer fabricates actual three-dimensional objects, one thin layer at a time, and then builds up hundreds or thousands of these layers on top of each other.

Some of the early 3D Printers made their fabrications by squirting out tiny volumes of liquid from tiny nozzles, just like a regular printer. And, just like a regular printer, those 3D Printers were controlled by a computer that follows instructions from a file. (One website that you can download files from is called "Thingiverse – Digital Designs for Physical Objects", and there are many others.)

Engineers call this process Additive Layer Manufacturing, but the more popular name, 3D Printing, is the one we'll probably be stuck with.

Grown Versus Made

Consider the bones of the human body. They are all gracefully curved and asymmetrical – and magnificently efficient. They are the minimum weight needed to carry their loads.

At the other end of the scale, consider the chunky manufactured parts that go into our cars and planes. They are usually made from rectangular or cylindrical parts – and are heavier than they need to be.

Imagine that we want to make, for example, the landing gear for a plane using 3D Printing. The first step is to work out where the stresses and loads will be. Then we can use 3D Printing to "grow" the landing gear. It will be made only of those sections that carry the load – and therefore a lot lighter. It will be more like our bones: perfect for the job.

In aircraft, a reduction in weight of one kilogram saves about $3500 in fuel over its lifespan.

EARLY DAYS

The first 3D Printers were called Rapid Prototyping Machines. They were used to make plastic prototypes of complex designs, because engineers wanted to see and hold a full-size model of what their final product would look like. Start-up companies and academics (many at the University of Texas at Austin) began making these machines in the late 1980s. For example, 3D Systems from South Carolina had their first commercially available Stereolithography machine in 1986.

Back then, a 3D Printer would deposit a thin layer of liquid resin and run a tiny ultraviolet beam over the surface in a specific pattern. The ultraviolet light would harden the resin in that pattern. The printer would put down another very thin layer, harden part of that, and keep on building it up. The unhardened resin would just drain away or be washed away. After several hours or days the final object, perhaps the size of a loaf of bread, would be ready. However, it would be made of a plastic resin, not the metal, wood or leather that the final manufactured object would be made of.

The other approach, also dating to the 1980s, was called Selective Laser Sintering. Powdered ceramic, metal or glass was laid out in a thin layer, and then melted and fused with a high-temperature laser. This would then be repeated, thin layer after thin layer, until the final object was made. (To make the laser's job easier, the chamber would be heated to about 10°C below the melting point of the material.)

WHERE WE ARE NOW

Since the 1980s, the field of 3D Printing, or Additive Layer Manufacturing, has advanced enormously.

For example, before Rapid Prototyping Machines, it used to cost Timberland US$1200 and take one week to hand-craft a sole for an upcoming shoe. Now it takes 90 minutes and costs US$35.

Today, there are many different types of 3D Printers.

Originally we were limited to using only liquids (plastics or resins) as the raw materials. Today, the raw materials that go into the Printers can be plastics (solid, liquid or granular), metals, ceramic powders, metal or plastic film, chocolate, icing sugar, silicone rubber, simple chemicals, concrete or paper. Even clothing has been Printed.

There are many different technologies to harden the raw material into the physical object – Ultraviolet Stereolithography, Selective

Laser Sintering, Electron Beam Freeform Fabrication, Direct Metal Layer Sintering, Fused Deposition Modelling, and so on.

The precision of Printing is usually limited to around one-tenth of a millimetre (about 100 microns), but that will improve with time.

Besides the convenience, 3D Printing can reduce waste enormously. Most of the material extruded or laid down ends up in the final product. This is quite different from the manufacture of, say, a laptop computer. Currently, that process starts with a solid block of aluminium, and then 95 per cent is removed by machining to leave behind the case and the internal ribs.

Old Cars

Jay Leno, the fabulously wealthy comedian and talk-show host, loves his collection of 190 or so motor vehicles. He keeps the older ones on the road with a 3D Printer.

He'll design a missing part from scratch, Print it, and try it in the car to see where it needs to be adjusted to fit better. He'll then incorporate these changes into the computer file and Print the revised part. He'll repeat this over and over until the plastic part fits exactly. He'll then give the plastic part to a machinist to make the part out of metal.

EXAMPLES OF 3D PRINTING

In 2011, European Aeronautic Defence and Space Company (EADS), the company that makes the Airbus, Printed a bicycle using Selective Laser Sintering. The raw materials were metal, nylon and carbon-reinforced plastics, in the form of a fine powder – leading to wheels, wheel bearings, axles and a frame. As we develop the technology to manipulate these materials down at the level of molecules, we'll be able to Print high-stress, safety-critical aviation components.

In 2012, British chemists Printed drugs. They first used a common bathroom sealing material to Print some Reaction Chambers – basically miniature eggcups. Then they squirted standard chemicals, via a US$2000 3D Printer, into these mini eggcups, which when combined in a simple chemical reaction gave a drug. They are now working on Printing the common anti-inflammatory drug ibuprofen. They have already shown how easy it is to Print chemical laboratory equipment.

> 3D Printing is the only technology we have that can make a functioning robotic hand. Even so, it took 24 hours to print all the parts and another 16 hours to assemble.

In 2013, the mobile phone company Nokia released 3D files of their flagship Lumia 820 handset so you can customise the case to suit yourself. You can have a waterproof, glow-in-the-dark phone with a built-in solar charger, corkscrew and bottle opener if that's what you want.

Also in 2013, engineers at Oak Ridge National Laboratory in the USA Printed a 600 gram robotic hand. It integrated a metallic skeleton with a titanium skin-like mesh, and had hydraulic pipes running through the skeleton. Let me emphasise that there were no pipes, hoses or drilled holes – the hydraulic fluid that powered the robotic hand ran through Printed ducts in the structure. Voids were deliberately left as the robotic hand was printed, layer by layer. The hydraulic fluid runs at enormous pressures to power the hand – 2000 tonnes per square metre. 3D Printing is the only technology we have that can make a functioning robotic hand like this one. Even so, it took 24 hours to Print all the parts for this first hand, and another 16 hours to assemble it. The engineers are developing a 3D Printer to fabricate the entire hand in a single piece.

A gun was Printed for the first time in 2013, on a US$8000 3D Printer. First, the separate components were Printed in ABS plastic, and then they were assembled into a white plastic gun. The firing pin was a simple household metal nail. The gun survived only half a dozen firings before self-destructing – but with those firings, it could have delivered a lethal wound. Within a week, over 100,000 copies of the computer files needed to make that gun had been downloaded.

All of that said, the technology is still young. The 3D Printing process can take a long time, both the quality and the surface finish can be variable, and it's still difficult to build complex objects from many different kinds of materials.

Mars Food

How do you feed astronauts on a 500-day mission to Mars? Using a 3D Printer, obviously.

In early 2013, NASA gave a US$125,000 grant to develop a 3D Printer that will print "nutritious and flavorful" food to Texas-based company Systems and Materials Research Corporation. The concept originated with an SMRC engineer who printed chocolate for his wife using a 3D Printer.
How sweet!

WHERE WE'RE HEADING

There are currently two major trends.

First, the technology has gone far beyond making plastic prototypes to making production runs of actual objects. For example, the giant aerospace company Boeing has printed some 22,000 parts for their jet planes, both military and civilian. Printed parts are used on both the F-18 Fighter Jet and the Boeing 787 Dreamliner Passenger Jet. Boeing's rival, Airbus, is trialling Printed parts for control surfaces, cooling systems, and lighter-weight brackets and landing gear components.

In 2013, the world's largest manufacturer, GE, announced they would use 3D Printing to make a fuel nozzle for their new LEAP jet engine. (They already have US$22 billion of confirmed orders for this LEAP engine.) 3D Printing would make obsolete the old production method of casting and then welding 20 small metal parts. Instead, the nozzles would enter life as a flat bed of cobalt-chromium powder. The plan is that a powerful laser would melt or fuse the powder in a layer, then another layer just 20 microns thick (0.2 millimetres) would be added. It would in turn be melted with the laser, and this process repeated until the final fuel nozzle was Printed. Each jet engine would use 10 to 20 nozzles, and the plan is to print 25,000 annually by 2016.

Second, the field has split.

At one end are the huge professional-grade 3D Printers that fill a warehouse. These are the ones used by the aerospace industry.

At the other end you can buy, for a few thousand dollars, an amateur-grade 3D Printer that can sit on a desktop. The cheap ones are currently basically a Toy, not a Factory. Slowly, and not very precisely, they will Print a plastic version of what you want.

But over time the price will come down, and the capability will go up.

Atoms

The Nobel-winning physicist Richard Feynman was asked to consider the hypothetical situation that all of our scientific knowledge had been lost. What would he write if he could pass only one item of information to future generations to help them get started again?

He said, "Everything is made from atoms."

Imagine if you could use individual atoms as your raw materials. Further down the line, a 3D Printer might have as its starting materials just the 92-or-so naturally occurring elements – Hydrogen, Helium, Lithium, and all the way past Sodium and Iron, right up to Uranium. Each element would be in its own little box. (There might be engineering problems with storing Fluorine and the radioactive elements – but Engineers are good at fixing problems.)

If you had the right "fusing" or "fixing" technology, you could potentially make anything.

THE FUTURE OF 3D PRINTING

The potential is enormous.

You could print off a metal gear to replace the broken one in your car's gearbox, or some of that extra-special lubricant for your bike chain. In a sudden killer-flu epidemic, you could print off enough antiviral drugs for your whole family. You could use one 3D Printer to make another identical 3D Printer, and so on, and so on (and so on).

In artificial hip joints, there is a metal ball-and-socket. The inner part of the socket has to be really hard and impervious, so

There are huge professional-grade 3D Printers that fill a warehouse but for a few thousand dollars you can buy an amateur-grade 3D Printer that can sit on a desktop.

that it doesn't wear. But the outer part, the section that binds to the bone, has to be porous, so that the bone will infiltrate and bind to it. The previous method was to make the socket from two different types of metal and then bond them together. However, with 3D Printing, you can make the socket from one piece of metal, just changing the porosity and density of the metal where it sits close to the bone.

Suppose we can have different materials in a single part. You could incorporate tracks that carry electricity or light, and even lots of sensors.

3D Printer in Space

NASA plans to send a 3D Printer to the International Space Station in 2014. It will have to be specially fabricated to be able to operate in microgravity. Astronauts will be able to Print spare parts, rather than wait for them to be sent up on the next resupply mission.

There will be social changes. At the moment, in the field of manufacturing, the countries that have the advantage are those with low costs and low wages. So manufacturing capacity may well shift around the world; although it's much too early to make specific predictions, we know that Manufacturing Capability will shift, but not to where, nor in what quantities. Another claim is that there will be no need for factories when any town, village or even house can have its own 3D Printer. However, if you want to make hundreds of pencils each minute, there are advantages in using a big factory with assembly lines.

There will be legal changes. If a manufactured item can be totally described and specified with a digital file, then that digital file can be copied. Once it escapes from the original manufacturer, how will they get their royalty or cut?

We could send these machines to an asteroid, and they could use the raw materials of the asteroid to build a home for us for when we eventually move into space.

Maybe the 3D Printer will be as significant as the printing press in 1450, the steam engine in 1750 or the transistor in 1950.

I might be wrong, but I think it will be a Game Changer.

Surgical 3D Printing

3D Printing has saved the life of a newborn baby.

The baby had a defective airway. The normal upper airways (the single trachea that splits into the twin bronchi) are reinforced so they don't collapse when you suck air in. This baby had a section of left bronchus that would collapse upon breathing in. By six weeks of age, he had difficulty breathing. By two months, he was kept alive only thanks to a tube forcing air into his tiny lungs.

A CT Scan gave enough information to Print an exact-size model of his collapsed upper airways. A fully absorbable splint was then Printed. It was a marvel of engineering – designed and fabricated for that one baby only. It resembled a vacuum cleaner hose, and could bend, stretch and even expand with his future growth. During surgery, it was wrapped around his collapsed left bronchus. He could breathe on his own within seven days, and he was sent home after twenty-one days.

Lung tissue should grow into the splint, which should totally resorb within three years. His breathing after that should be normal.

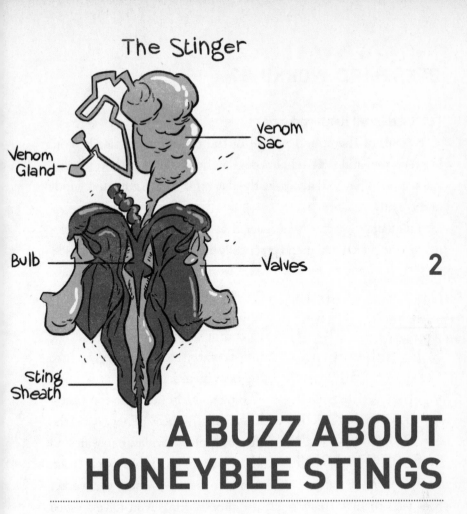

The Stinger

Venom Sac

Venom Gland

Bulb — — Valves

sting Sheath

A BUZZ ABOUT HONEYBEE STINGS

We might not know a lot about insects in general, but we all "know" two facts about honeybees. First, they are very hard-working creatures, and second, when they sting you, they die. Well, only the second part is true.

It seems reasonable to assume that honeybees are hard-working. After all, to make just one single kilogram of honey, honeybees have to make a total of some 10 million separate visits to flowers to collect the nectar. In the course of those 10 million visits they cover a total distance equal to 10 trips around the Earth. In the USA honeybees produce an average of about 29 kilograms of honey per year in each of some 5 million hives.

BEES HARD-WORKING?

But are they all hard-working?

Not all of them, and not all of the time. Bees typically work between two and twelve hours per day, depending on their job and the season. They will also take the day off if it's too cold, too windy or too rainy.

The female worker honeybees that leave the hive to forage for nectar and pollen will spend practically all the daylight hours outside. The workers back at the hive have many duties – clustering together to warm the hive or fanning their wings to cool it down, taking care of the honeycombs, etc. But they do take frequent breaks.

> In her life of six to nine years the Queen Bee produces about one egg each minute, or 1200 to 1500 per day. That works out to laying her own bodyweight in eggs each day!

The male drones have the easiest life of all the bees. They leave the hive only after midday, party around for a while in packs, and then return to the hive where the worker bees feed them – that's right, the drones don't even have to feed themselves!

Furthermore, bees are not the busiest creatures, not compared to hummingbirds and shrews, which have to eat their own bodyweight every day just to survive.

However, bees have been used as a role model for "being busy" since the 15th century. In Chaucer's *Canterbury Tales* the phrase "busy as bees" is applied to women who labour mightily to deceive men.

Bee Sleep

Bees don't sleep the way we do (for one thing, they don't have eyelids to shut). But they stay stationary, let their muscles relax and allow their antennae to droop.

One study even claimed that, on average, honeybees spend only about 20 per cent of the time working – and the rest of the time they just hang around and chill out.

Mind you, the Queen Bee really does know what hard work is. In her life of six to nine years she produces about one egg each minute, or 1200 to 1500 per day. That works out to laying her own bodyweight in eggs each day! On the other hand, she does spend a lot of time lying down . . .

BEE GENDER 101

Now, to understand why the honeybee has to die after she stings you, you need to realise that bees come in three "genders" or "sexes" or "orientations".

First, there is one Queen, who is the only fertile female in the hive. Each of her fully developed ovaries has about 170 tubular ovarioles, which is where the eggs develop.

Second, there are about 60,000 sterile female workers in the average hive. They have ovaries which are not fully developed, and which carry only 4 to 12 small ovarioles. They will usually only lay eggs if there is no Queen. The workers cannot mate with the male drones, so their eggs will not get fertilised, and will develop only into undersized male drones – never a female Queen or female workers.

From birth to about Day 3, the workers clean the hive. By Day 5 of their lives, they become nursing bees because certain glands have matured inside their mouths. By Day 12, their wax-making glands are functioning, allowing them to make structures in the hive to store nectar and honey. Around Day 19 of their lives they begin guarding the hive with their stingers. By Day 21, they are halfway through their short lives and have begun to leave the hive to forage for nectar and pollen. And then around Day 42 workers usually die.

Male drones make up the third gender living in the hive, perhaps 1000 or so of them per colony. They don't have a stinger, and they can't collect nectar. Luckily, they are fertile and can make sperm. The Queen will mate once in her life with half a dozen of these drones, and then their usefulness is over.

GIVE IT UP FOR THE HIVE

Insect stings are common and painful – and only very rarely fatal. A 1981 poll in the UK revealed that 10 per cent of people are stung each year by bees or wasps, with only 0.7 per cent of these experiencing severe symptoms. In the USA, about 17 people die each year from bee stings. (This is usually from a very rare anaphylactic reaction, when the human Immune System overreacts.)

So how come a female worker honeybee has to die when she stings you?

First, her stinger has little one-way barbs on it, so once it goes into your flesh she has no choice in the matter: she can't pull it out again.

Second, the stinger is connected to a sac full of venom, and her digestive tract, and some muscles and nerves. After she has stung you, her little stinger (along with the entire end segment of the bee's abdomen) stays in your flesh, even if you scrape her body off you. There are enough "smarts" wired into the nerves and the muscles that surround her venom sac to keep it pumping venom. Her venom sac can keep pumping without her body or even her head. Unfortunately, she dies from a case of massive abdominal rupture, as all her bodily contents squirt out of the big hole where her stinger used to be.

CUI BONO? (WHO BENEFITS?)

The obvious question is: "For what purpose?" Who benefits when a honeybee stings you and then dies?

The clue is the fact that the female worker honeybee is sterile. She cannot pass on her genes to future generations. The only way that she can ensure the survival of her DNA is by protecting her sisters, and that includes her big sister the Queen, back in the hive. So she gives up everything for the good of the hive.

> There are perhaps 1000 or so male drones per colony. The Queen will mate once in her life with half a dozen of these drones, and then their usefulness is over.

At the same time as she stings you, she also squirts out special alarm pheromones. Pheromones are hormones that travel through the air – and these alarm pheromones excite other worker bees. In their excited state they will sting anything that moves near them.

So the act of stinging an intruder brings on a very kinetic and maximal response from the rest of the hive.

SCRAPE OR PULL OUT STINGER?

This is a case of people giving you the Right Advice (kind of), but for the Wrong Reason.

Should you pull the stinger vertically out of your flesh, or should you flick it off sideways, or scrape it off? The Standard Answer is that you should scrape it off, because (supposedly) if you pull it out with your thumb and forefinger, you will squirt more venom into your flesh.

The Correct Answer, verified by Three Experiments, is that you should get the stinger out as soon as possible. This is because the bee's nerve cells tell the muscles that surround the venom sac to keep on contracting therefore squirting venom into your flesh. You see, it's the contraction of these muscles around the venom sac that causes the venom to squirt into you – the pressure exerted by your thumb and forefinger makes no difference.

The Three Experiments were conducted by entomologists Dr P. Kirk Visscher and Richard S. Vetter. They bravely allowed themselves to be stung by bees, and to be injected with bee venom – always into their own arms. They did this many times, under varying conditions.

> So if you get stung, just get the stinger out as soon as possible. The essential factor is to not delay. The longer you wait, the bigger the weal.

First, the bee venom. The bee stinger and venom sac contain about 150 micrograms of bee venom. But only a small fraction of this is injected into the flesh when a bee stings you. Dr Visscher was injected with varying amounts of bee venom – between 1 and 100 micrograms. The result was as expected. As the dose increased, so did the size of the resulting weal (red raised area) on the arm.

Second, the two entomologists "collected a worker honey bee as she flew from her hive, grasped her by the wings, and pressed her against the skin of the inside of the volunteer's forearm until she stung". They then waited for two seconds before removing the stinger – either by scraping it off with the edge of a credit card, or by pinching the stinger between thumb and forefinger and pulling it out. There was no difference in the size of the weal raised on the skin from either pulling or scraping.

The third Experiment was to repeat the second Experiment but simply wait for varying times, up to 8 seconds, before removing the stinger. As you would expect, the longer they waited the bigger the weal raised – and, again, there was no difference between scraping and pulling.

So if you get stung, just get the stinger out as soon as possible. Scrape it off with your fingernail, or your credit card if you have one handy, or use some medical forceps if (by wonderful timing) you have a pair in your hand. The essential factor is to not delay. The longer you wait, the bigger the weal.

And if by scraping you happen to leave part of the stinger in your flesh, don't worry. In the experiments this did not increase the area of the weal, and there were no long-term effects. (Mind you, the sample size – two people – was very small. Who wants to volunteer to be stabbed by a bee?)

SHE WORKS HARD FOR THE HONEY

So out of the 60,000 bees in the hive, it's only the Queen that works hard for the honey all day long. But don't forget that it's the workers that are prepared to take a dive for the hive . . .

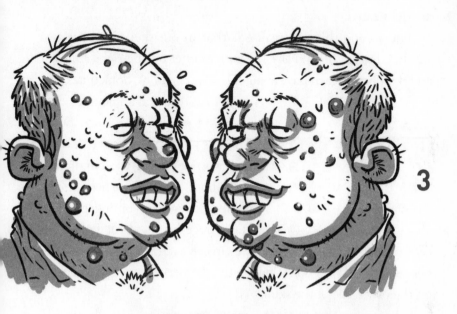

3

ABOUT FACE . . .
ATTRACTIVENESS

One of the factors that makes us humans special is our wonderful hands with their opposable thumbs. On average, about 90 per cent of us prefer to use our right hands, leaving the left-handers in very much a minority at about 10 per cent of the population.

But what about our faces? Did you know that one side is more attractive than the other?

LEFT VERSUS RIGHT 101

The first thing to realise is that this whole "left–right" thingie is a little fuzzy.

Sure, 90 per cent of us are right-handed. But 80 per cent are right-footed and 70 per cent are right-eyed while only 60 per cent are right-eared.

The second thing to realise is that in our skulls we have two separate brains, one on the left and another on the right. Our left and right brains each have about 50 billion neurons. Sometimes they work together, and sometimes they work independently of each other. There is a bundle of nerves joining the two sides – but the bundle has only about 250 million nerves. The number of nerves joining the two brains together is about half a per cent of the total number of nerves inside each brain. So, often the nerves in one brain don't "talk with" the nerves in the other brain on the other side of the skull.

> Our faces are not symmetrical – the right side of your face is a little different from the left side of your face.

One result is that our faces are not symmetrical – in other words, the right side of your face is a little different from the left side of your face. Charles Darwin noticed this asymmetrical pattern in human faces way back in 1872. He saw that when a person sneered, the canine tooth was exposed – but usually only on one side of the face.

This difference increases as you get older. The famous designer Coco Chanel supposedly said: "At 20 you have the face that God gave you, at 50 you have the face that you deserve."

Third, our brains are cross-wired to our bodies.

What this means is that our left brain mostly controls the right side of the body, and vice versa. Similarly, the muscles on one side of your face are controlled by the nerves on the other side of your brain.

Brain and Emotion

How is the brain specialised to deal with "emotions"?
There are two main neurophysiological theories.

One says that the left brain (which controls most of the right face)
is specialised for positive emotions, while the right brain (which
controls most of the left face) handles negative emotions.

The other theory says that the right hemisphere
overwhelmingly deals with the perception and expression
of emotions – regardless of whether they are positive or
negative emotions. These emotions then show themselves
on the left face. And, indeed, some research shows that
the left face is more active and intense during voluntary
emotional expression.

There is now a lot of support for this latter theory.

THE EXPERIMENT

So, now let's look at a study that tried to work out which side of our face
was more attractive. This study was carried out by Kelsey Blackburn and
Professor James Schirillo at Wake Forest University in North Carolina.

They photographed 20 volunteers (aged 35 to 65, 10 male, 10 female)
on both the left and right sides of their faces. They did this not from
the centre front, nor from totally side-on (at 90° from the centre line).
Instead, they took their pictures from more than halfway around – from
about 53° away from the centre line. Now, of course, there would be
some viewers who simply preferred the look of the "mostly right face", or
the look of the "mostly left face". To deal with these people, Blackburn
and Schirillo used Photoshop to mirror-reverse the sides of the faces.

They got 37 undergraduate psychology students to become "viewers", with the duty of rating the attractiveness of these photos. But the researchers did more than just ask the viewers what they thought. They also examined the pupils of their viewers' eyes to see if they changed in size when rating each side of the face for attractiveness. You see, it's pretty well established that the size of the pupil is related to the emotional intensity that an image evokes in you.

So the students were each shown four sharp images of two people. The images had all the colour removed, so they were just various shades of grey. (This was to exclude the effect of the retina responding differently to different colours.) Two images were an untouched right side of the face and an untouched left side of the face. The other two were a mirror-reversed right side of the face (which was actually the left side before it had been Photoshopped) and a mirror-reversed left side of the face (which was actually the right side).

LEFT IS LOVELY

The viewers then rated the faces in terms of how "aesthetically pleasing" they were. Least pleasing was "1", neutral was "5", while most pleasing was "10".

In general, the viewers preferred the left side of the face of both the men and women.

This was regardless of whether they were shown an untouched "genuine" left side, or a left side that had been mirror-reversed to look like a right side. This was also independent of the gender of the person in the photo and of the gender of the person doing the judging. And the pupils of the volunteers opened a little larger when they rated the faces more attractive.

This left-side attractiveness is seen (to some degree) in portraits. For example, Dr I.C. McManus examined nearly 1500 portraits painted in Western Europe between the 16th and 20th centuries.

He found that about two-thirds showed the left side of the face, while just one-third showed the right side.

Thanks to the wiring of your brain, it's your left side that best shows your emotional state.

More recently, a study has shown that between the ages of 10 and 20 years, girls spend twice as much time looking at themselves in the mirror as boys do.

I expect that it's at this time that they learn how to put their best face forward . . .

Left Versus Right Armpit Sweat

In my early days of doing live TV, I used to get nervous before the show. Very consistently, my right hand would get very cold and my right armpit would sweat rivulets down the inside of my upper right arm. I put this down to the fact that I was using the "Intellectual" side of my brain – the left side – and that I was having a minor "stress attack" (OK, perhaps a Sympathetic Nervous Response) on the right side of my body. Over several years, my right-side body response gradually moderated.

One day, in the Green Room, I ran into a Belly Dancer before she went on air. We got talking, and she told me that she was nervous. A Belly Dancer, as an artist, would presumably use the "Emotional" side of the brain – the right brain. I asked if I could feel her hands – and sure enough, her left hand was freezing, while her right hand was normal. I tactfully enquired about her armpits – and she told me she was sweating rivers from her left armpit.

4

ALCOHOL AND ARTIFICIAL SWEETENERS

It sounds strange, but a rum with diet cola will get you drunker than a rum with regular cola.

THE EXPERIMENT

Let's suppose that we give alcoholic drinks to two identical twins. These twins were not only born identical, they have also lived identical lives, even down to eating the same food and having identical exercise programs – so they have identical weights. In our hypothetical experiment, the twins are perfect controls for each other.

The plan is to give each twin a drink containing the same amount of alcohol (that is, ethanol, not the poisonous methanol) to see what happens. In each case, it's not pure alcohol but alcohol mixed with something sweet. And here's the only difference: one twin gets normal soft drink as the mixer, containing about 65 grams of sugar (sucrose); the other twin has the same brand of soft drink, but without the sugar – that is, with a zero-calorie artificial sweetener.

Empty Calories

Isn't 65 grams a huge amount? You wouldn't add 65 grams of sugar to a cup of tea or coffee. That's a lot of so-called Empty Calories – in the sense that it contains energy, but no nutrients.

In 2011, world sugar production was 168 million tonnes – about 24 kilograms per person for that year. That works out to about 65 grams per day – which, by a coincidence, is the amount of added sugar in the mixer alcoholic drinks in this study.

Driving home in their two identical cars, the twins both get tested for blood alcohol level thanks to a Police Random Breath Test. (The Police don't have to be identical twins, but the Breath Testing Units are – that's Science and Engineering for you.)

The result is amazing. The twin who drank alcohol mixed with the sugared soft drink can legally drive – his Blood Alcohol comes in at 0.034, well under the limit of 0.05 for a driver on a full Australian licence. But the twin who drank exactly the same amount of alcohol mixed with the zero calorie artificial sweetener is measured at 0.053. That's 56 per cent higher! He's just over the legal limit, and it's off to the Cooler for him.

DIET IS DANGEROUS?

What's going on? How can the twins have different Blood Alcohol Levels if they drank exactly the same amount of alcohol?

It's mostly due to the emptying rate of the stomach.

Your stomach will push out its contents into the next section of the gut, the small intestine, at what is pretty well a fixed rate of about 8 to 12 kilojoules per minute (or 2 to 3 kilocalories per minute). The food in the stomach can (in general) empty only at this rate. In other words, the presence of food in your stomach will increase the time it takes for your stomach to empty. In the case of alcohol with added sugar, the stomach will take longer to move the alcohol into the small intestine – it treats the regular sugared drink as "food". (Actually, it's a little more complicated than just the energy content. The "osmolality" is another factor, being about 30 milliosmoles per kilogram for "diet" soft drinks versus 700 milliosmoles per kilogram for "regular" soft drinks.)

In 2011, world sugar production was 168 million tonnes – about 24 kilograms per person for that year. That works out to about 65 grams per day.

In one study at Royal Adelaide Hospital, volunteers drank 30 grams of alcohol, or about three so-called Standard Drinks. The energy content was about 940 kilojoules (225 kilocalories).

One group had their alcohol mixed with a zero-calorie artificial sweetener, so the total energy content was still about 940 kilojoules. The average volunteer stomach could push half of this load into the small intestine in about 21 minutes.

But the other group had a regular, fully sugarised mixer with their alcohol. The total energy content was more than doubled, to about 2000 kilojoules. With this extra load of energy to deal with, the average of the volunteers' stomachs took about 35 minutes to push half of its load into the small intestine.

Thanks to the extra time to process the sugar, the peak Blood Alcohol level was less – which is why one hypothetical twin was under the legal limit, and the other one over it.

This finding has been backed up by later studies. One found that drinkers' motor skills were impaired more if they drank the alcoholic drink with the zero-calorie mixer. You wouldn't want to have a car collision because you were drunker than you thought. However, in this study these drinkers were not aware of their bad performance.

NEW KNOWLEDGE

The vast majority of us – and that includes me – have no idea that a rum with diet cola will get you drunker than a rum with regular cola.

And yet, this turns out to be part of the essential knowledge you need to survive in Western Society. Here, alcohol is more or less all-pervasive, being present at most social occasions. In fact, pre-mixed alcoholic drinks are popular with the younger generation, especially women, who for many and varied reasons often adopt Low Energy diets.

Now that you know that diet mixed drinks get you drunker, you should try to use this information for good, to know how to drink more responsibly. After all, as Mary Poppins said, *"A spoonful of sugar helps the medicine go down"*.

Empty Stomach

There's an old saying, "Never drink on an empty stomach."
If you do, you will get more drunk, and more quickly,
than if you have some food in your gut.

The presence of food in the stomach can reduce peak
Breath Alcohol Concentrations by as much as 57 per cent.
This is yet another reason to give up drinking before breakfast.

5

BIORHYTHMS: A NEW EQUATION

All living creatures evolve and adjust themselves to the regular rhythms of the Universe around them. Creatures that live on the seashore follow the tides. We humans prefer to sleep at night, in the dark – this preference is commonly called the "body's natural clock". So it's not surprising that people study Circadian Rhythms, which have lots of scientific credibility. It's true, for example, that we feel a little sleepy at mid-morning and mid-afternoon.

However, the so-called "Biorhythm Theory" tries to use this credibility to propose that humans are subject to three cycles that oscillate in our bodies and control our lives.

There's absolutely no hard evidence for this.

There are many wild and incorrect
claims made in Biorhythm literature.

For example, " . . . in Germany and Switzerland . . .
no surgical operation will be performed by a
doctor when the patient's biorhythm position
is in an unsupportive constellation".

And even more rubbish: ". . . the Japanese or Swedish
would never schedule surgery on a patient whose Physical
cycle was below the critical line! . . . The Japanese airline
companies will not permit pilots to fly an airplane
if they are in a critical cycle."

HISTORY OF BIORHYTHMS

The study of Biorhythms began with Wilhelm Fliess in the late
19th century. He was a medical doctor, a friend and patient of
Sigmund Freud, and an amateur numerologist. He was obsessed with
the numbers 23 and 28, because he found he could express any other
number in terms of 23 and 28. For example, $12 = (23 / 2) + (28 / 56)$

This convinced him that these two numbers ruled the Universe.
The number 28 was "obviously" related to the menstrual cycle,
so he called it "Female" – and that left 23 as the "Male" cycle.
Unfortunately, he didn't know enough Number Theory to realise
that any number can be expressed from any other two numbers that
don't have a common divisor!

In the 1920s, the Austrian Alfred Teltscher, Professor
of Engineering at the University of Innsbruck, "felt" that his
students' work waxed and waned periodically. So he added the

33-day Intellectual Cycle to the 23-day and 28-day cycles.

Soon afterwards, evidence was found for real Biological Rhythms in humans. And yes, birds do migrate at certain times of year, cicadas follow 13-year and 17-year cycles (see "Cicadas Hit Their Prime" on page 55), and so on.

These real cycles gave credence to these fake Biorhythms.

REAL CIRCADIAN RHYTHMS

In 1927, Curt Paul Richter, director of the Psychiatry Clinic at Johns Hopkins University, wrote a paper in which he discussed the concept of biological clocks, such as those that govern sexual behaviour, eating and so on. He was doing genuine scientific research into body rhythms, and kept right away from these unproven 23-, 28- and 33-day cycles.

Over the next half-century, researchers discovered that hormones are released in rhythms – for example, cortisol (the stress management hormone) is released in a daily rhythm, while hormones from the pituitary gland in the brain are released roughly every 80 minutes.

So, evidence grew for genuine Circadian Rhythms. If you've ever had a long-haul flight on a jet, you've probably experienced Jet Lag. This happens when your own internal Circadian Rhythms don't match the day–night cycle in your new location.

GULLIBLE ME

In the 1970s, I bought two books promoting Biorhythm Theory. Being very gullible, I believed everything they claimed. George Thommen wrote *Is This Your Day? How Biorhythm Helps You Determine Your Life Cycles*, while Bernard Gittelson wrote *Biorhythm: A Personal Science*. He also wrote *Biorhythm Charts for the Famous*

> ### Biorhythm Theory said that all humans were subject to three clearly defined cycles: Physical, Emotional and Intellectual.

and Infamous and *Biorhythm Sports Forecasting.*

I now realise that these authors combined carefully selected "research" with volumes of unproven anecdotes to give masses of unwarranted speculation. Their "Biorhythm Theory" said, rather unoriginally, that all humans were subject to three clearly defined cycles.

The three cycles were a Physical Cycle (23 days: strength, hand–eye coordination, endurance, resistance to disease, etc.), an Emotional Cycle (28 days: passion, empathy, intuition, love/hate, optimism/pessimism, etc) and an Intellectual Cycle (33 days: memory, concentration, intelligence, alertness, reasoning ability, etc). Without any measurements or proof of any kind, each author claimed that the cycles started on the day you were born and, furthermore, that they continued relentlessly and uninterrupted through life. These cycles oscillated between "High" and "Low" – sometimes above, and sometimes below, a central "Zero Line".

These cycles were suspiciously easy to interpret.

When a particular cycle was "High", you were sane, and excelled in the attributes of that cycle. When you were "Low" in a specific single cycle (for example, Emotional), you should take a box of tissues with you at all times.

According to the theory, erratic behaviour resulted from a cycle changing from "High" to "Low" – as it crossed the "Zero Line". During this "Critical Day" or "Transition Period", your "life energy" was claimed to be in a "state of uncertainty". Your behaviour became more erratic when two cycles simultaneously crossed the "Zero Line". When all three cycles crossed the "Zero Line" on the same day, you probably shouldn't have gotten out of bed.

By the mid-1970s, many video arcades had a Biorhythm machine that would print out your personal charts based on your date of birth, and many newspapers ran a Biorhythm Chart next to the Horoscope Column. In the 1980s, there were Biorhythm Apps for early Personal Computers, and you could even buy handheld Biorhythm Calculators, such as the Kosmos 1 and the Casio Biolator.

REALITY BITES

As I was deeply and madly in love with this Biorhythm Theory, but also being scientifically inclined, I plotted my Physical, Emotional and Intellectual curves and compared them to what actually happened in my life. After a few months I found, much to my despair, hardly any correlation between my actual cycles and my predicted Biorhythm cycles. I gradually stopped plotting the curves and stopped believing!

Since then, scientists have investigated the "Biorhythm Theory" – and found it very much wanting. All the papers that supported "Biorhythm Theory" had major statistical and methodological errors. Furthermore, no reputable scientific journal has published any papers supporting it.

> In the 1980s, there were Biorhythm Apps for early Personal Computers, and you could even buy handheld Biorhythm Calculators.

After all, why should your Biorhythms start exactly on the day of your birth? Your heart was beating for several months before you were born.

Why do men and women share the same 23- and 28-day physical and emotional cycles? Surely men are, in some ways, "different" from women, and this should show itself in the cycles?

Why should your Biorhythms never vary? After all, women's menstrual cycles vary. What if you had a fever or a coma, and were unconscious for a day or two?

And why should everybody have exactly the same three cycles?

Why doesn't at least one person have a 25-day or 30-day cycle?

And finally, if the three cycles all start at birth, then they should meet again after 58 years and 66 days. How come we haven't noticed this to be a significant period of "rebirth"?

RECYCLE

Today, the Biorhythm Theory is nowhere near the Top of the Pops, as it was in the 1970s. It turns out the Biorhythm just ain't got that swing. You can still buy Biorhythm software for your computer, and a few die-hards still promote it, but the average gal on the street has probably never even heard of it!

Today, Biorhythms have gone into the Recycling Bin. Maybe they just oscillated themselves out of existence . . .

6

BLOOD–BRAIN BARRIER

The human brain is very special – and not just because it's probably where we think that we think. It's guarded by an almost impervious cellular barrier that doesn't exist anywhere else in the body – the so-called Blood–Brain Barrier.

And now scientists are trying to sneak through this barrier – to treat currently untreatable Central Nervous System (CNS) diseases.

These CNS diseases affect over 1.5 billion people worldwide. According to the World Health Organization: "CNS disorders will be the greatest medical need of this century as no CNS disorder is currently treated adequately and the number of people in the world with CNS disease is set to increase sharply in the decades ahead."

Furthermore, if the ageing-population trend continues, half of all the people alive in 2100 will show Alzheimer's symptoms.

We don't understand the Blood–Brain Barrier – but we need to.

Why Can't We Treat CNS Diseases?

There are three main reasons why we can't adequately treat diseases of the Central Nervous System.

First, the human brain is staggeringly complex. Our knowledge of it ranges between mostly incomplete and barely rudimentary.

Second, the negative side effects of CNS drugs often limit their use.

Third, the Blood–Brain Barrier blocks most medications anyway. And if they do get into the brain, it usually pumps them back into the main blood circulation.

WHAT'S SPECIAL ABOUT THE BRAIN?

It's fair to say that our brain is "the most complicated organisation of matter known". And to help it do its remarkable work, it needs an especially stable and well-controlled environment.

That 1300 grams inside our skull is fed by some 650 kilometres of blood vessels. These blood vessels twist and loop around to always be close to our 100 billion or so nerve cells, as well as ten times as many "glial" cells – which "support" the nerve cells. The nerves are organised into a fiendishly complex three-dimensional array of inter-connecting fibres. Each nerve is connected electrically to several thousand other nerves. Electrical changes can ripple along them at speeds of up to 400 kilometres per hour.

It takes a huge amount of energy to run our human brain. It weighs just 2 per cent of the body weight, but takes 20 per cent of the body's energy and 20 per cent of its blood supply.

The capillaries that feed the brain cells are about 5–10 microns in diameter. (In comparison, a hair is about 70 microns across.) Between them, the brain capillaries have a total surface area of 12 to 18 square metres – a huge area for interchange of chemicals.

But these brain capillary vessels are different from all the other blood vessels in our body. They are lined by a strange structure called the Blood–Brain Barrier. It closely controls what is, and is not, allowed to leave the blood supply and enter the brain. For example, the chemical *glutamate* is found in food, and therefore appears in the bloodstream. But glutamate also acts as a neurotransmitter, so the Blood–Brain Barrier carefully manages its access into the brain to ensure it stays at acceptable levels.

The Blood–Brain Barrier helps maintain the very stable environment that is essential for our very complicated brain to work reliably. It makes the brain a Walled City. It's your own personal Customs and Border Security.

HISTORY OF THE BLOOD–BRAIN BARRIER

We got the first hint of the existence of the Blood–Brain Barrier back in 1885, when German bacteriologist Paul Ehrlich injected a coloured dye into the bloodstream of living animals. At autopsy, he found that the dye stained the entire body – except the brain and spinal cord. He wrongly thought that the Central Nervous System didn't absorb this particular dye.

In 1913, his student Edwin Goldman did the "other half" of the experiment. Goldman injected the same dye into the fluid that surrounds the brain – the cerebrospinal fluid (CSF). The dye stained the brain, but no other part of the body. This was the first hint that there was a barrier between the Blood and the Brain to stop "stuff" from travelling between the bloodstream and the brain.

In 1900, the German neurologist Max Lewandowsky injected doses of potassium ferrocyanide into dogs. A small dose into the CSF caused convulsions, but a larger dose into the blood did nothing. This was another hint at the existence of a brain barrier.

In your body, the tiny capillaries are where all the action happens. The bigger blood vessels just circulate the blood to and from the capillaries.

In 1921, the Russian neurophysiologist Lina Stern realised that if tetanus got into the bloodstream, it could be stopped by the anti-tetanus serum. But once the tetanus got into the CSF, the serum no longer worked. Somehow, the tetanus could cross an unknown barrier, but the anti-tetanus serum could not. During World War II, she developed techniques to bypass this barrier by injecting drugs directly into the brain.

There was lots of soft evidence for the existence of a barrier. But it was only after the invention of the first primitive Electron Microscope in the 1930s that in 1969 we finally proved the existence of the Blood–Brain Barrier – by actually visualising its components.

Dalton

The "dalton" (named after the chemist John Dalton) is the standard unit for measuring the mass of atoms or molecules. It's defined as exactly 1-twelfth of the mass of a carbon atom. So a hydrogen atom is about 1 dalton, carbon exactly 12 daltons, and oxygen about 16 daltons.

By comparison, a molecule of aspirin is around 180 daltons and water around 18 daltons. The molecule that carries iron into the brain, transferrin, is about 80,000 daltons.

ANATOMY OF THE BLOOD–BRAIN BARRIER

We used to think of the Blood–Brain Barrier as some kind of simple biological flyscreen. If the chemical was small enough (with a molecular weight of less than 500 daltons), it could get through the tiny holes and into the brain. But if the chemical was bigger than 500 daltons, it was excluded.

This was our simple (and incorrect) belief.

We now know that the Blood–Brain Barrier is not just a mesh with little holes in it, but a vital and dynamic organ made of many different types of cells. It constantly responds to local changes and requirements – adjusting the brain's food supply, making local repairs, increasing the defences against invaders, and so on.

Leaky Capillaries

In your body, the tiny capillaries are where all the action happens – where the blood "talks to" each organ. The bigger blood vessels (arteries, arterioles, venules and veins) just circulate the blood to and from the capillaries.

It may come as a surprise to you, but the capillaries in your body are leaky. In fact, they have to be leaky – otherwise they couldn't deliver Good Stuff to your organs and take Bad Stuff away.

The capillary walls come in four grades – from very leaky to slightly leaky. The capillaries in the Blood–Brain Barrier are only slightly leaky.

PHYSIOLOGY OF THE BLOOD–BRAIN BARRIER

The Blood–Brain Barrier has four major functions.

It finetunes the internal environment of the brain very closely. It protects the brain from what's outside. It tells Immune System cells what to do in response to local changes. It also allows a constant supply of nutrients for the very hard-working brain.

So, like Customs and Border Security, the Blood–Brain Barrier has to control what goes in and what comes out.

There are five major routes of transport for "stuff" across the Blood–Brain Barrier. They are all variants of either straight through the endothelial cells that line the blood vessels, or around them.

NEUROLOGICAL DISEASE AND THE BLOOD–BRAIN BARRIER

In some cases, CNS disease leads to increased leakiness of the Blood–Brain Barrier. Stroke and traumatic brain injury, as well as Alzheimer's and Parkinson's Disease, all do this.

In other cases, the increased leakiness of the Blood–Brain Barrier seems to be the cause of the disease. "Multiple sclerosis, infectious meningitis and meningoencephalitis, cerebral malaria, dementia associated with AIDS, epilepsy, and possibly some neuro-developmental diseases such as schizophrenia and autism" all seem to be caused by excessive leakiness, according to Alan M. Palmer.

For example, we know that Alzheimer's Disease involves having too much of a molecule called beta-amyloid in the brain. The Blood–Brain Barrier has one protein to bring the beta-amyloid out of the bloodstream into the brain, and another protein to do the opposite. What if modifying these proteins to keep the excess beta-amyloid out of the brain slowed down the progression of Alzheimer's Disease? This is one simple example of how understanding the Blood–Brain Barrier could help us deal with a significant disease.

Invading the Brain: Shrinking

If you squirt a chemical called mannitol into the bloodstream leading into the brain it sucks water out of the endothelial cells, making them shrivel. The Tight Junctions between the flat endothelial cells in the Blood–Brain Barrier will open up – but only for about 40 to 120 minutes. It's not a very long time, but it allows you to increase the amount of drugs that get into the brain by up to 100 times.

Dr Edward A. Neuwelt, a neurosurgeon at the Oregon Health and Science University's Blood–Brain Barrier Program, has been finetuning this technique for two decades. In 2007, Joanie Lafferty, a 57-year-old mother of three, was paralysed on the right side of her body – this was caused by a cancer that had spread to the brain. Dr Neuwelt used his technique on Ms Lafferty, immediately following up the mannitol with the anti-cancer chemical methotrexate. After two treatments, she walked from the hospital without a wheelchair. After 12 once-a-month treatments, she is still in remission in 2013.

There are a few disadvantages with this technique. First, it's expensive. Second, it's risky, because you alter which chemicals normally get into the brain, including toxins that would usually be filtered out by the kidneys. Third, because it affects the entire brain, it can cause tissue swelling, toxicity and infection. And fourth, it requires huge expertise by the people who do it.

BARRIER TO TREATMENT

The vast majority of today's medications cannot cross the Blood–Brain Barrier in significant quantities. Mind you, a tiny 2 per cent of drugs, such as most antipsychotics, sleeping aids and antidepressants, are smaller than 500 daltons and can sneak through.

Today, neuroscientists have come up with a handful of ways of getting the other 98 per cent of therapeutic drugs across the Blood–Brain Barrier.

Invading the Brain: Drilling

Back in 2001, William Pardridge, a scientist at the University of California in Los Angeles specialising in the Blood–Brain Barrier, studied the effect of a stroke on rats. A stroke is when part of your brain dies – either because the blood vessel gets blocked and not enough oxygen gets through, or a blood vessel bursts open and blood leaks into the surrounding brain tissue, damaging it. He had a drug that could reduce the damage caused by a stroke.

He deliberately blocked a brain artery in his rats, causing them to have a mini-stroke. He then drilled a hole through the skull and injected his drug into the brains of some of the rats. This treatment reduced the volume of the brain damage caused by the stroke by 70 per cent.

It worked for the rats in this very experimental study, but you can see the problems with doing this type of study on human beings.

BUSTING THE BARRIER

There are currently three main ways to cross the Blood–Brain Barrier: Invasive, Pharmacological and Physiological.

Invasive techniques are physical. They mechanically bypass the Blood–Brain Barrier. They can involve physically delivering a drug to a specific area of the brain via flexible catheters, or implanting the drug in the brain and letting it diffuse out over time. Invasive techniques also include shrinking the endothelial cells to open up the Tight Junctions, or using multiple focused ultrasound beams to disrupt the barrier.

The Pharmacological Approach is to modifty the drug to mimic the attributes of molecules that already freely enter the brain. Some small molecules, such as alcohol, nicotine and benzodiazepine, will diffuse easily into the brain – if they are less than 500 daltons, and have various appropriate properties (for example, like or hate fat, have charge or do not have charge, etc). Unfortunately, the modifications needed to allow crossing of the Blood–Brain Barrier usually mean that the drug no longer works as it originally did.

> Pardridge deliberately blocked a brain artery in his rats, causing them to have a mini-stroke. He then drilled a hole through the skull and injected his drug into their brains.

The Physiological Approach involves using the myriad transport systems that endothelial cells already have built into them.

So, one basic method of getting drugs into the brain involves encapsulating them in fat so that they can sneak through the fatty walls of the endothelial cells. Unfortunately, the balls of fat usually get stuck to the fatty walls.

A more sophisticated approach is to use the internal baggage-handler molecules that ferry needed chemicals into, across and out of the endothelial cells. We can alter the baggage-handler molecules to carry a different cargo, or we can add extra cargo (which is called the Trojan Horse technique, after the Greek legend).

These baggage-handler molecules are a bit like spacecraft – they're very big, but they carry very few passengers. In some cases, this doesn't matter because you don't need to deliver a large amount of drugs – but some diseases need to be treated with large quantities of drugs.

WHERE DO WE GO?

If there is one simple take-home message, it's that we know less than a microscopic percentage of all we will have to learn over the next few decades about the Blood–Brain Barrier. We need that knowledge before we can effectively manipulate the Blood–Brain Barrier to prevent or treat diseases of the brain.

Imagine how different our society would be if our nursing homes weren't full of people with Alzheimer's Disease, or if a stroke was just something like a broken leg, where you merely had to rest up for a while and heal before you fully recovered.

The Blood–Brain Barrier would turn from a High Wall into a Small Hurdle, and our currently incurable diseases of the brain would be just a temporary inconvenience.

No Blood–Brain Barrier

Some parts of the brain (the pineal gland, the posterior pituitary, etc.) are specifically not protected by the Blood–Brain Barrier.

This is so the brain can quickly sample various chemicals from the bloodstream. It can then respond by secreting hormones directly and speedily into the bloodstream – without having to navigate through a Blood–Brain Barrier. The brain can also sense a threat (a killer rabbit, a vampire) or something nice (a meal, a kiss) via its other senses – and again respond with various hormones directly into the blood.

It makes sense to have some parts of the brain unprotected by the Blood–Brain Barrier. On the other hand, the lack of protection means that they are more at risk from invaders, such as toxins or viruses.

Bacteria into the Brain

It's always been a mystery as to how bacteria (which are relatively huge) can get across the Blood–Brain Barrier. For example, how does *Neisseria meningitidis* cause cerebrospinal meningitis? The mystery was solved in 2009 by Mathieu Coureuil.

The bacterium *Neisseria meningitidis* can live in the human nasopharynx. It can then enter the blood circulation and, while in the blood, stick to the blood-side of an endothelial cell in the Blood–Brain Barrier. It sticks thanks to special hairs (or "pili").

It then uses these pili again to send "confusing signals" to the Tight Junctions between the endothelial cells. Once the Tight Junctions open, the bacteria cross the Blood–Brain Barrier and invade the coverings of the brain – the meninges. There, they form colonies and cause inflammation – and often fatal meningitis.

7

CICADAS IN THEIR PRIME

In a good-sized plague, 10 trillion cicadas can suddenly appear from underground – about 1400 cicadas for each person on our planet. For a few weeks, there can be up to 300 cicadas per square metre, with a temporary total of over 20 million tonnes of insect life. (That's on par with the combined weight of all the people in the USA.) The cicadas' liquid excrement will fill some 300 Olympic-sized swimming pools per day. After they die, they leave behind some 500 trillion eggs – about 1000 times more than there are stars in the Milky Way.

These are very impressive numbers. And research into cicadas also gives us an additional way of finding Prime Numbers.

PRIME NUMBERS 101

Prime Numbers are the "basic building blocks" of all natural numbers. This is called the Fundamental Theorem of Arithmetic.

The Greek scientific writer, poet and astronomer, Eratosthenes of Cyrene, became the first person to calculate the circumference of the Earth, 2300 years ago. While dabbling in maths, he invented the famous Sieve of Eratosthenes – an easy method of finding Prime Numbers.

Prime Numbers are numbers that can be divided only by themselves and 1. So 2, 3, 5, 7, 11, 13 and 17 are all Prime Numbers – but 18 is not a Prime Number, because you can divide it by both 2 and 9.

To activate the Sieve of Eratosthenes you write down all the numbers from 1 to as high as you want to go. Then simply strike out every second number that comes after 2, every third number following the number 3, and so forth. All the numbers that remain will be Prime Numbers. It's called a Sieve because all the Numbers that are not Prime just "fall through".

You'll also find Prime Numbers in the life cycles of cicadas.

Prime Facts

First, around 300 BC, Euclid proved that there are infinitely many Primes – in other words, there is an infinite number of Prime Numbers.

Second, every number can be expressed as a product of one or more numbers that are each Prime Numbers – and in a way that is unique for each number (except for the order of the Prime Numbers).

For example:

$$23,244 = 2 \times 2 \times 3 \times 13 \times 149$$
or
$$10 = 2 \times 5$$

So, Prime Numbers are the "basic building blocks" of all natural numbers. This is called the Fundamental Theorem of Arithmetic. This sounds very obvious, but it took a genius like Carl Friedrich Gauss to prove it in 1801.

Third, the Prime Number Theorem says that the probability of a number n being Prime is inversely proportional to its number of digits (or to the logarithm of n). For example, the number X has a high chance of being Prime, while the number XY has a lower chance, and XYZ even lower again.

However, that's as close as we get to a formula to predict Primes. In 1975, the number theorist Don Zagier wrote that Primes "grow like weeds among the natural numbers, seeming to obey no other law than that of chance [but also] exhibit stunning regularity [and] that there are laws governing their behaviour, and that they obey these laws with almost military precision."

CICADAS 101

Cicadas are an unruly mix of noise and chaos, with lots of sex and babies thrown in for good measure. There are about 1500 species of cicadas known, with more remaining to be discovered and described. Most of these species appear yearly in midsummer, but there are also the rather special so-called "periodic" cicadas. They appear at Prime

Number intervals – most commonly 13 and 17 years, but sometimes at 7-year intervals.

The cicadas are part of the insect order Hemiptera. They are sucking insects that pierce plants with their pointy mouthparts and suck out the juices. They have two pairs of membranous wings and five eyes – three simple eyes (ocelli) and two prominent compound eyes.

The cicada breeding cycle begins when huge numbers of adult cicadas emerge in the spring. They have to be quick, because even though they have been underground for up to 17 years, their remaining life expectancy is now only two to six weeks. They mate within a week, and a few days later the female lays her eggs. She drills into the green twigs of trees and inserts up to some 400 to 600 eggs. This drilling can weaken fruit tree twigs, and as the tree matures the weakened twigs can sometimes break under the load of fruit.

These eggs hatch after two to ten weeks. The little babies, known as nymphs, make their way down to the ground by crawling or dropping, dig their way into the soil with their claws and begin the next phase of their lives. They live underground, at depths between 5 and 50 centimetres. For the next 7, 13 or 17 years, they will suck the juices from the roots of shrubs and trees. There are huge numbers of nymphs but, luckily for the tree, they each have a low metabolic rate and grow very slowly. The 17-year cicadas are almost fully grown as nymphs by eight years, but they continue to feed underground until the 17th year. During their underground stay, they usually undergo five moults – they abandon their current exoskeleton when it becomes too constricting.

When the ground gets warm enough, they come out of the soil and attach themselves to any nearby tree or post with their sharp claws. Their shells split open down the back, the adults emerge, and they plunge into their above-ground life for only a few weeks before dying.

Cicadas Kill Interweb

In Japan in 2006, cicadas mistook Fibre Optic cable for branches. So they punctured the cables with their sharp ovipositors – long and pointed organs 1 millimetre in diameter specialised for the laying of eggs – and laid their eggs inside.

Besides repairing the damage, the Japanese redesigned the Fibre Optic cables with an extra protective layer, and without the external grooves that attracted the cicadas.

DEAFENING CICADAS

Male cicadas make noise in the same way that a "wobble board" does. They have a pair of "timbals" (special circular rigid snapping plates) on the abdomen which they can buckle, making a noise. These timbals generally resonate at between 120 and 480 hertz, but some small species resonate faster, producing songs so high in pitch they can't be heard by human ears. As a special adaptation to make them louder, there are large tracheal air sacs that open to the outside to act as resonators. Cicadas can generate sound at 120 decibels, which is easily enough to give humans permanent hearing loss.

Male cicadas make three separate types of noise.

They make the Disturbance Squark when they are disturbed, attacked or captured. They make a rather attractive noise when they are mating, known as the Courtship Song. And they make a different noise, the Congregational Song, after permanently leaving their underground homes. This song is influenced by the songs of other cicadas and by the weather. It helps co-ordinate the arrival of cicadas above-ground.

Female cicadas make a much quieter noise by clicking their wings together. This signals their approval of a male.

WHY PRIME CICADAS?

Biologists have asked for a long time whether it's just a coincidence that the emergence periods of the three species of periodic cicadas (7, 13 and 17 years) are all Prime Numbers.

You can see that if cicadas run on different cycles, and if these cycles are Prime Numbers, the cicadas will meet each other only very rarely. For example, a 13-year cycle and 17-year cycle will meet only every 221 years. When both species of cicadas emerge above-ground, there would be huge competition for food – but only once every 221 years. The rest of the time, there would be enough food.

Professor Mario Markus, a physicist from the Max Planck Institute for Molecular Physiology in Germany, sees another benefit to cicadas emerging from underground after a Prime Number of years. It's protection against periodic predators – predators that appear on a regular cycle, such as birds, and the Cicada Killer Wasp.

> Biologists have asked for a long time whether it's just a coincidence that the emergence periods of the three species of periodic cicadas are all Prime Numbers.

Let's start by assuming that the cicadas emerge every 12 years. Then the predators that come out every two years will attack them, and so will the predators that come out every three years, four years and six years. But, according to Markus, "if the cicadas mutate to 13-year cycles, they will survive".

So Markus and his colleagues created a mathematical model. In this mathematical model, if prey happens to be met by a predator, then it loses. According to this model, as the years roll by, the length of the cycle increases until the cicadas hit a Prime Number, and then it stays there. Huge numbers of cicadas appear, and there simply aren't enough predators to eat them all.

This model has an unexpected and delightful side effect. It turns out to be a machine, like the Sieve of Eratosthenes 2300 years ago, which can generate Prime Numbers. It's not very quick at generating these Primes, but it rather prettily merges two apparently unrelated fields – Number Theory and Population Biology.

Large Prime Numbers are rare, and they're difficult to find, but a biological mathematical model like this, based on cicadas, will click through the non-Prime numbers, and land on the Primes – and that will leave the mathematicians chirping.

2013 Prime Discoveries

2013 was a wondrous year, with not one but *three* major discoveries about Prime Numbers.

First, on 25 January, Dr Curtis Cooper proved that $2^{57,885,161}-1$ is a Prime Number. This monster number has over 17 million digits, and it's the largest Prime Number yet discovered. If you printed it in an average book, it would run to some 5000 pages.

Second, Twin Primes. Twin Primes are pairs of Prime Numbers that differ by two. For example, 17 and 19 are Twin Primes, as are 101 and 103. For thousands of years mathematicians have asked themselves if there is an infinite number of such Twin Primes only two digits apart. As of late-2013, we don't know.

But on 13 May 2013, the mathematician Yitang Zhang proved there is an infinite number of pairs of Primes that are only 70 million digits apart. Further refinement of his work has proven there is an infinite number of pairs of Primes that differ by only five million digits.

To a non-mathematician, being out by a factor of 2.5 million – for example, getting the answer "five million" instead of "two" – seems a lot. But remember, the jump between five million and two is inconsequential compared to the jump from five million to infinity.

Third, the Goldbach Conjecture (or at least one "version" or "form" of it) was proven. In 1742, the Russian mathematician Christian Goldbach wrote a letter to the Swiss mathematician Leonhard Euler, proposing a Conjecture. This Goldbach

Conjecture comes in two forms – the Weak and the Strong.
They are easy to state, but extraordinarily difficult to prove.

The Strong Form proposes that every even
number greater than two is a sum of two Primes.
For example, 36 = 17 + 19. This has never been proved.

The Weak Form is that every odd number greater than
seven is a sum of three Primes. For example 13 = 3 + 5 + 5.

In June 2013, it was announced that mathematician
Harald Helfgott had finally proved the Weak Form.
So that leaves only the Strong Form to be proved.

8

CLUELESS

Averages are funny things. If you ask a whole bunch of people how they would rate themselves as a car driver, the overwhelming majority would confidently say they are better than average. But that's impossible. The average is the midpoint, so half of the drivers have to be better than average, while the other half have to be worse.

So some people must be unable to appraise or evaluate their own skills accurately. And that's what David Dunning and Justin Kruger found way back in 1999, with their paper entitled "Unskilled and Unaware of It: How Difficulties in Recognizing One's Own Incompetence Lead to Inflated Self-Assessments". So when people are incompetent, not only do they make mistakes, but "their incompetence robs them of the ability to realise it".

This is the famous "Dunning – Kruger Effect".

HOW NOT TO ROB A BANK

In their paper, they tell the story of the bank robber McArthur Wheeler, who in 1995 walked into two separate banks in Pittsburgh in the USA to steal money in broad daylight. He wore no disguise or balaclava and, indeed, went out of his way to locate and smile at the surveillance cameras. The police broadcast the surveillance tapes on TV, and he was arrested that night. He was flabbergasted that he had been caught, and protested, "But I wore the juice." He had been told that if he first rubbed his face with lemon juice, the cameras could not see or register his face.

And he had proved it – at least to his own standards. As an experiment he had rubbed lemon juice on his face and held his Polaroid camera at arm's length to take a photograph of his own face. Unfortunately, he had probably accidentally rotated the camera upwards so that he took a photo of the ceiling – but, because his face was not in the photo, he was convinced that the lemon juice had made his face invisible to cameras.

Now, Mr Wheeler is an exceptional case, but we all know people who are truly incompetent, yet are so totally unaware of it that they actually believe they are better than average. People from all walks of life consider themselves above average, including business managers, students, 97 per cent of university professors who think they are better than the average university professor, and, of course, practically everybody who drives a car.

EXPERIMENT – DELUSION

Back in 1999, Dunning and Kruger tested psychology students on their abilities in grammar and logic – and then they asked the students to rate themselves on how well they thought they'd performed. As you would expect, there was a Bell Curve, with most of the students performing around the middle, and smaller numbers doing really well or really badly.

Surprisingly, the students who did badly thought they had done well. Yes, the students in the bottom 12 per cent actually estimated that they were in the top 38 per cent. In grammar or logic, the skills needed to provide the correct answer are the same skills you use to evaluate if the answer is correct. According to Dunning and Kruger, these students could neither give the correct answer, nor recognise when they were wrong.

The students who did very well made the opposite mistake – they thought that they had performed worse than they actually had. They reckoned that they were in the top 32 per cent, but actually were in the top 14 per cent. Dunning and Kruger put this down to the False-Consensus Effect. The better students thought that all the other students were as good as they were, and so believed that they hadn't performed particularly well.

So the bottom students had a problem with how they rated themselves, while the top students had a problem with how they rated others.

EXPERIMENT – TRAINING

Dunning and Kruger followed up with two more experiments.

First, they got the bottom and top groups of students to grade the exams of their fellow students. The bottom students gained no insight at all. They still thought they had each individually done well – they still could not recognise their own incompetence. But the top students, who were competent, immediately saw how well they had done relative to their fellow students – and so re-rated themselves closer to reality.

Second, Dunning and Kruger gave the students some training in Basic Logic. That changed things for *everybody*. Both the bottom students and top students now rated their abilities closer to their real abilities. Education was the key – in this case. The underachievers suddenly realised how incompetent they really were and became more realistic in their self-evaluations.

Insight over the Ages

Sufferers of the "Clueless Effect", studied by Dunning and Kruger, carry a double burden. Not only do they make mistakes, they are too incompetent to realise it – and to see how badly they perform generally.

But this is an age-old problem.

Confucius wrote, "Real knowledge is to know the extent of one's ignorance."

In Shakespeare's *As You Like It*, we find: "The fool doth think he is wise, but the wise man knows himself to be a fool."

Alfred North Whitehead observed, "It is not ignorance, but the ignorance of ignorance that is the death of knowledge."

Thomas Jefferson wrote, "He who knows most, best knows how little he knows."

Charles Darwin followed along the same lines with: "Ignorance more frequently begets confidence than does knowledge."

SELF-DELUSION IS EVERYWHERE

But of course, nothing related to the human brain is simple.

Suppose you give the students different grades of tests – some easy and some hard. When the task is easy, the top students rate their performance more accurately, but when it is hard, those in the bottom lot are better at realistically rating themselves.

Another complication is that this Dunning–Kruger Effect – where the unskilled and incompetent rate themselves more highly – seems to happen only in the West, not in Asian countries.

> The underachievers suddenly realised how incompetent they really were and became more realistic in their self-evaluations.

In one study, Japanese and American volunteers were given a first task, at which they either failed or succeeded. They were then given a second task. If they had failed at the first task, the Japanese volunteers put more time into the second task. In the same situation, American volunteers did the opposite. They worked on the second task for a shorter time.

Another study looked at co-operation skills. They tested how students balanced "self-interest" against "co-operation" in an artificial test, and then how they rated themselves. In this study, 84 per cent of the students said they would help or co-operate with their fellow students – but only 61 per cent did. Again, another example of self-delusion.

Yet another study looked at how easy it was to manipulate students' impressions of their performance. The exam was in American Geography. The students were individually taken aside before the exam. Half were asked easy Geography questions, and were led to believe they were quite knowledgeable. As a result of this bolstering of self-esteem, these students sat the test and thought that they had done well in it. As you now might expect, it was the opposite for the other half. They were asked difficult questions, were led to believe they didn't know their American Geography, and later reported that they thought they had done badly in the exam. However, the overall results were actually very similar.

Perhaps the philosopher and scientist Bertrand Russell got it right back in 1951, when he said, "One of the painful things about our time is that those who feel certainty are stupid, and those with any imagination and understanding are filled with doubt and indecision."

Nobel or IgNobel

In the year 2000, Dunning and Kruger were awarded the prestigious IgNobel Prize in Psychology for their research.

A few years later, I was also a recipient of the IgNobel Prize in Interdisciplinary Research for my ground-breaking research in Belly Button Fluff and why it is almost always blue. Harvard University showed me so much respect that they flew me all the way to Harvard at my own expense – they didn't want to insult me by offering to pay for my travel, food or accommodation.

Inability to Recognise Disease

Anosognosia is a curious disease. For example, if it paralyses the left side of your body, it stops you from realising this.

The awkward name comes from the Greek words "nosos" meaning "disease" and "gnosis" meaning "knowledge", and finally the "a" at the beginning flips the meaning to the opposite.

Anosognosia involves massive denial of your malady. So if a doctor is assessing you and asks you to lift a coffee cup with your (paralysed) left hand, you find you cannot do it. But you might say that you didn't hear the doctor, or that you are tired, or that you have already had your coffee for the morning and don't want to have any now.

Perhaps the Dunning–Kruger Effect is the psychological version of anosognosia.

9

COCKROACHES' BITTERSWEET REVENGE

Cockroaches have been around for a very long time. In fact, between about 300 and 360 million years ago (during the Carboniferous period, when a lot of coal beds were laid down), roach-like insects made up about 40 per cent of all insect species. You'd imagine that after all that time, they would pretty well have got their design down pat – but they are still evolving today.

Squashed Cockroach

If you've ever looked at a cockroach after you've squashed it, you might have noticed a white pulpy mass filling much of the abdomen.

This is the "fat body", and is mostly composed of two types of cells. First, there are the adipocytes, which are filled with fat and act as a food supply when times are bad. Second, there are the mycetocytes, which are packed full of bacteria (*Blattabacterium*).

There's a mutual symbiotic relationship between these bacteria and the cockroach they live inside. If you kill the bacteria with antibiotics, the cockroach will become unwell and is likely to die. If you kill the host cockroach, the bacteria will die.

These bacteria have been colonising cockroaches for at least 140 million years. Strangely, they are already inside the cockroach before it hatches from the egg. We think that these bacteria help cockroaches with their diet by recycling nitrogen.

So next time you squash a cockroach, don't be disgusted by the white mass oozing out – instead, marvel at its complexity!

COCKROACH 101

Today there are some 5000 species of cockroach – but only a few of them live in our houses. In general, the big guys (*Periplaneta americana*, up to 40 millimetres long) are the American Cockroach while the little guys (*Blatella germanica*, up to 16 millimetres long) are the German Cockroach.

They are difficult to control because they reproduce very quickly, are active at night when we are asleep, and live in nooks and crannies that we can't get to. They can go for a month without food, and will eat each other if times are tough.

German Cockroaches have another survival trick – some of them have evolved to *not* like sweet foods.

Now, most forms of life like sweet stuff. "Sweet" usually means some kind of sugar, and sugars mean easily digestible food. This is why we used sugars to attract cockroaches.

Back in the old days, you had to "deal" with a cockroach via the Shoe Method or, if you were squeamish and wanted a bit of distance, a rolled-up newspaper. Then we invented poisonous sprays that would kill the dreaded cocky. And after that we invented baits. These were little packets of sweet stuff to attract the cockies, with a hidden deadly load of poison. But then the cockroaches began avoiding the sweet-tasting baits.

How did they know to avoid the sweets?

CRAZY COCKROACH TASTE

Some of the German Cockroaches have somehow switched around their chemistry of tasting, so that sugar now tastes bitter instead of sweet. As a result, when they come across a poison bait tasting of lovely sweet glucose, they avoid it – because the "taste" of sweetness makes them unhappy.

Big Question: how do cockroaches taste the world around them? Cockroaches don't have tongues loaded with tastebuds like we do. No, they have little "tasting" hairs all over their bodies – legs, feet, wings and, yes, around the mouthparts. Inside these hairs are specialised receptor cells that respond to "sweet" or "bitter".

Dr Coby Schal and his fellow entomologists from North Carolina State University looked very carefully at the tasting hairs around the cockroaches' mouthparts.

Let's call the German Cockroach populations that hate glucose the "Glucose-Averse" Cockroaches. As for the Regular Cockroaches that love glucose, let's call them Regular Cockroaches.

> Cockroaches don't have tongues loaded with tastebuds like we do. They have little "tasting" hairs all over their bodies.

Dr Schal's team found that in Regular Cockroaches some of these receptor cells would respond only to glucose, while others would respond only to something bitter, such as caffeine. Furthermore, in the Regular Cockroach, the receptor cells that responded to bitter would not respond at all to glucose – and vice versa. This is exactly what you would expect.

But the situation was very different in the cockroaches that run away from sugar – the Glucose-Averse Cockroaches. Give these guys some glucose and, yes, the glucose-sensitive receptor cells fire – but more weakly than normal. As for the receptor cells that should respond only to bitter – there was a huge surprise. Somehow, the chemistry had been turned around. In the Glucose-Averse Cockroaches, not only would these bitter-sensitive cells respond to glucose, they would do so more strongly than the glucose-sensitive receptor cells would do.

So, overall, what happens when the Glucose-Averse Cockroaches taste glucose? The glucose-sensitive hairs fire weakly while the bitter-sensitive hairs fire strongly. Result? The cockroach brain is flooded with the sensation of bitterness. The Glucose-Averse Cockroaches don't eat the sweet poison. Instead, they run away and live – and have lots more babies, who inherit this glucose-hating behaviour.

COCKROACH EVOLUTION THEORIES

Now, there are three theories about how this rapid evolution could have happened.

First, there's a theory that out of the untold billions of German Cockroaches that live in cosy harmony with us, a few spontaneously had a mutation that turned the sensation of sweetness into bitterness. The Regular Cockroaches died because they ate the poison, while the mutated ones survived and bred very rapidly to fill the empty ecological niche in our kitchens.

The second theory is that there already was, from the distant past, a section of the cockroach DNA that hated glucose. After all, while in most cases "sweet" means "food" and "bitter" means "poison", there are some sweet poisons called "glycosides". (Perhaps in the past – one, 10, 100 million years ago – some plants had evolved sweet-tasting poisons to protect themselves?) Maybe this section of the cockroach DNA was sitting there quietly, waiting to be reactivated in case cockroaches came across some sweet-tasting poisons in the future.

And the third theory is that perhaps the German Cockroaches bred with other cockroaches that already had this mutation.

We don't yet know which theory is correct . . . or if there's another explanation that hasn't been theorised yet.

As for the Mutated German Cockroach, the result is mixed – they get to live, but they don't enjoy the sweet things of life. Imagine having to give up a whole Food Group. It's a bittersweet victory for the cockroaches . . .

Mosquito Tastes Poison?

Each year, malaria infects over 200 million people and kills about a million of them. Malaria is caused by the *Plasmodium* parasite. We humans catch it by being bitten by a female *Anopheles* mosquito which has already been infected by the *Plasmodium* parasite. When she bites us, the *Plasmodium* parasite gets into our bloodstream and so we get infected.

For a while, we dealt with this mosquito by spraying surfaces with insecticide. But now the mosquito has learned to avoid landing on those surfaces.

Perhaps by learning more about how the German Cockroach "tastes" the world around it, we can learn how the mosquito tastes the world, and therefore stop it from spreading malaria.

In mid-2013, Professor Leslie Vosshal at Rockefeller University took a step in this direction. She successfully altered an odour receptor on the mosquito *Aedes aegypti*. This mosquito carries dengue fever and yellow fever. As a result of the alteration, she produced a generation of mosquitos that can't sniff out humans.

10

DARK ENERGY

The 2011 Nobel Prize for Physics was awarded for the discovery of Dark Energy. While Dark Energy is not simple, there are five Take-Home Messages I can give you.

First, Dark Energy is real. (A few different methods of measurement agree.)

Second, we have no idea what Dark Energy actually is. (Hence the name "Dark".) But there are a few main contenders at the moment.

Third, Dark Energy pushes. It has a repulsive (or outwards) force. So it makes the entire Universe (which is already expanding) expand faster. It's currently expanding 25 per cent faster than it was five billion years ago.

Fourth, it is evenly spread throughout the Universe. More of it is created as the Universe expands. So its repulsive force is always increasing. (However, there's a fixed amount of "matter", which is thinning out as the Universe expands.)

And finally, Dark Energy is huge. It makes up about 69 per cent of all the mass/energy in the Entire Universe. (About 5 per cent of the Universe is made up of "Regular Matter", while about 26 per cent is made up of the poorly understood Dark Matter – see pages 95 to 103). But we discovered Dark Energy only as recently as 1998. How could we miss 69 per cent of everything for so long?

To quote one of the Dark Energy Nobel Laureates, Brian Schmidt: "If you have to 'make up' 95 per cent of the Universe, you probably don't understand what you're doing."

Nobel Prize

A reporter once asked a Nobel Prize winner if they could explain their Nobel Prize in one sentence. The Nobel Laureate replied, "If I could explain it in one sentence, it wouldn't be worth a Nobel Prize."

Another version of this comes from the Nobel Laureate, Richard Feynman: "If I could explain it to the average person, it wouldn't have been worth the Nobel Prize."

Regardless of all that, I'll be brave and give it a go.

THE BIG BANG AND AFTERWARDS . . .

As I said, Dark Energy is complicated, so let's go there in three big, loose steps.

Let's start with a Timeline of our expanding Universe from the Big Bang onwards, follow that with an explanation of the "regular" expansion of the Universe, and then finish off with how Dark Energy made this expansion accelerate even faster.

By the way, we don't know what was there before the Big Bang – we have lots of theories, but no hard data. But we do have the timing of a handful of events after the Big Bang.

A TIMELINE OF OUR EXPANDING UNIVERSE

Very soon after the Big Bang came the Inflationary Epoch. And I do mean *soon*. It ran from 10^{-36}–10^{-32} seconds after the Big Bang. (By the way, "10^{-36} seconds" is scientific talk for one millionth of one millionth of one millionth of one millionth of one millionth of one millionth of a second.) It gets its name because during this Epoch, the Universe "inflated" extraordinarily quickly.

> We don't know what was there before the Big Bang – we have lots of theories, but no hard data.

During this Inflationary Epoch, the Space–Time Fabric of the Universe expanded at faster than the speed of light. The Universe expanded from a size much, much smaller than a proton to about the size of a grapefruit – a size range of at least 10^{78} (or a million times a million, and repeat 11 more times). By the way, at this point the Universe was so "hot" that there was no matter, only energy.

We don't know what caused this Inflationary Epoch. We don't know why, after expanding so rapidly, it suddenly slowed to a much smaller rate of expansion. But because of it everything that made up the Universe got spread out over a much bigger volume – and that goes for all the lumps and bumps in the early Universe. The result was that the lumps and bumps got much smaller and smoothed out. So today's Universe appears pretty well the same, no matter in which direction we look.

After the Inflationary Epoch, another notable stage was 3 to 20 minutes after the Big Bang. Protons and neutrons began to join up to make the nuclei of atoms, in the process of nuclear fusion. Energy congealed to make matter as the Universe cooled. After 20 minutes, this nuclear fusion stopped because both the temperature and the density of the Universe had dropped too much.

About 377,000 years after the Big Bang, the temperature had dropped so much that electrons could stick to nuclei. So atoms of hydrogen and helium began to form, without electrons in between them – and so the Universe became "transparent". For the first time, radiation could now travel freely for long distances before colliding with electrons and being absorbed. The photons of radiation that were present at this time are the same photons that we can see in the Cosmic Microwave Background Radiation.

About 400 million years after the Big Bang, the first stars formed. The Universe was still expanding.

About 8.8 billion years after the Big Bang (about 5 billion years ago), the effects of Dark Energy started to dominate. The rate of expansion of the Universe began to increase.

Approximately 9.1 billion years after the Big Bang (about 4.7 billion years ago), Gravity drew a cloud of gas and dust together to form our planet, Earth.

And finally, 13.8 billion years after the Big Bang is Today. You are here, right now.

TV and the Big Bang

In the old days when you tuned your analog TV to an empty non-broadcast channel, you would see "white noise". About 2 per cent of that white noise on the TV screen was made by photons that had been travelling since the Universe was just 377,000 years old.

Maybe we could keep one digital TV channel re-broadcasting that analog white noise, just for old times' sake?

"REGULAR" EXPANSION OF THE UNIVERSE

Back in the 1920s, the astronomer Edwin Hubble announced his discovery that the Universe was expanding. The galaxies were moving further apart.

There is a very subtle, but very important, point to understand.

The galaxies were not moving further apart because they were travelling across Space–Time. No. On average, the galaxies were staying put relative to Space–Time – but the actual fabric of the Universe was expanding. (This is not strictly correct, but it's OK as a First Approximation.)

Imagine that you glue some tiny cheap jewels onto the rubber skin of a partially inflated balloon. You then inflate the balloon a bit more. The jewels are moving apart. But the jewels are not moving relative to the rubber. Instead, the rubber is stretching apart and carrying the jewels with it. In the same way, the Space–Time Fabric of the Universe is expanding – and, as it expands, it carries the galaxies further away from each other.

Back in the 1920s, Hubble used the new 100-inch Mount Wilson telescope to look at galaxies. He measured their Doppler Shift (the change in frequency due to the speed of the galaxy). He found that practically all galaxies were moving away from us. This shifted the colour of their light towards the red end of the colour spectrum – hence the term "Red Shift". Hubble also found that the further away a galaxy was, the bigger its Red Shift.

Since the 1920s, astronomers have assumed (thanks to Gravity doing its "sucking" thing) that this expansion would mellow and slow down.

> Hubble found that practically all galaxies were moving away from us. This shifted the colour of their light towards the red end of the colour spectrum.

But in May 1998, cosmologists held a conference called "The Missing Energy in the Universe". Some of them presented data showing that the Universe had – strangely – increased its rate of expansion about 5 billion years ago. (Apparently, the Universe is bigger and emptier than we had previously thought.)

Of the 60 scientists at the conference, 40 accepted the revolutionary new findings. This was very unusual – Scientific Conferences do not generally poll scientists to see if they accept new or controversial findings. The Science of "Dark Energy" was just beginning – like a newborn baby.

DARK ENERGY – EXPLODING STARS

You might ask, how did astronomers measure that the Universe was expanding at a decreasing rate until about 5 billion years ago, but then gently began to expand at a faster rate?

Answer: they used exploding stars as a Standard Candle.

Let's look at both parts of the answer. What do we mean by "exploding stars"?

There are a few different mechanisms by which stars can explode. Our astronomers looked at Type 1a Supernovae, which start off as White Dwarfs. A White Dwarf is a "degenerate" star that has finished its normal burning and is now in the later stages of its life. This White Dwarf stage is the end point of evolution for certain stars – ones that started off with a mass between 8 and 10.5 times greater than the mass of our Sun. The White Dwarf star has cooled down and collapsed. It is about the size of our Earth, but has roughly the mass of our Sun, so it's very dense (about one tonne per millilitre). There are about eight White Dwarfs in the nearest 100 star systems.

To make a Type 1a Supernova, put a White Dwarf and a big star in a tight orbit around each other. The White Dwarf "sucks" some hot gas from the bigger star onto its surface. Once this layer gets a metre or two thick, and the White Dwarf reaches a mass about 1.38 times the mass of our Sun, the whole star explodes like a giant hydrogen bomb. The White Dwarf erupts outwards at about 5000 to 20,000 kilometres per second. After three weeks the explosion reaches about 10 billion times the brightness of our Sun, and then fades over the next few months.

> A White Dwarf is a "degenerate" star that has finished its normal burning and is now in the later stages of its life.

We have discovered that the longer the light lasts, the brighter the Supernova is. But they are all close to the same brightness, because they explode at around the same mass.

And what do we mean by "Standard Candle"?

A major part of Astronomy is measuring the distance to stars, galaxies and the like. But how do you tell the difference between a faint star that is close, and a bright star that is distant?

Luckily, Type 1a Supernovae all pretty well reach the same maximum brightness (after you correct for how long they burn). So if it's bright, it's close. If it's faint, it's far away. This is how a Type 1a Supernova can make a reasonable Standard Candle. We can measure its actual distance by its brightness. Its Red Shift will give us its "supposed" distance.

Two separate teams of astronomers (High-Z Supernova Search led by Brian Schmidt in Australia, and the Supernova Cosmology Project led by Saul Perlmutter in California) measured many Type 1a Supernovae. The younger and closer ones were where they were expected to be. But the older and more distant ones were not – they were fainter and further away. It was as though the expansion rate of the Universe had sped up about five billion years ago.

Energy is Mass, and Vice Versa . . .

How can "Dark Energy" be 69 per cent of the Mass/Energy of the Universe?

Well, astronomers first measured by how much the rate of expansion of the Entire Known Universe had increased. Then, they calculated how much energy you would need to make this happen. (Not surprisingly, it turns out to be a huge amount of energy.) When you convert this "Energy" into "Mass", this "Mass" works out to be about 69 per cent of the mass of the Universe.

Second, how can "Energy" be counted as "Mass"? Einstein showed us the way with his famous equation:

$$E = mc^2$$

where "E" is energy, "m" is mass, and "c" is the speed of light.

So you can think of "Energy" as being "activated mass", or "Mass" as being "congealed energy".

WHY FIVE BILLION YEARS AGO?

Why did the effect of Dark Energy show itself only five billion years ago? Why not earlier, or later?

It's because there has always been a battle between Gravity (an "attractive" force) and Dark Energy (a "repulsive" force). About five billion years ago was when Dark Energy finally got bigger than Gravity.

First, Gravity. Gravity is caused by the Regular Matter and Dark Matter present in the Universe. Gravity has always been trying to slow down that expansion of the Universe. But the effect of Gravity has been decreasing as the Matter in the Universe has thinned out.

Second, Dark Energy. Dark Energy seems (it's not proven yet) to be an inherent property of Space–Time. There seems to be a certain amount in each cubic metre of the Universe. As the Universe expands, it "creates" more Space–Time. Therefore, it also creates more Dark Energy (according to some Theoretical Physicists).

About five billion years ago was when the repulsive effect of Dark Energy began to outweigh the attractive effect of Gravity.

However, the amount of this Dark Energy in any given cubic metre of the Universe is very small. It's roughly a millionth of a millionth of a millionth of a millionth of a millionth of the matter in our planet's crust. But space is very, very big, so over the whole Universe Dark Energy adds up to about 69 per cent of everything.

WHERE NEXT?

One Big Question is: "What is the Universe expanding into?" One slightly facetious answer is: "The future".

Another Big Question is: "What happens in the future?"

In the short term – the next billion years – the Sun will heat up so much that Life on Earth will be hard pressed to survive.

In five billion years, our Sun will expand to swallow Mercury, probably Venus and possibly Earth.

But in the long term, Dark Energy will dominate.

BIG CHILL

What ultimately happens all depends on what Dark Energy turns out to be. If the amount of Dark Energy in each cubic metre is constant, then the Universe will thin out and space will be cold and empty. The rest of the Universe will disappear from view. This is called the Big Chill.

In 100 billion years, the clusters of galaxies that fill the sky will stretch to breaking point, leaving us with isolated clumps of galaxies, separated from each other by huge emptiness. The relative speeds of separating galaxies will be faster than the speed of light – so we won't be able to see them. Our home galaxy (long merged with Andromeda) could be the only galaxy visible in an otherwise empty Universe.

Inside our galaxy, the parsimonious low-mass stars will burn their fuel slowly, but only for 10 to 20 trillion years. New stars will occasionally form, but most of those will burn out within 100 trillion years. In a Cosmic sense, it will truly be the Big Chill.

BIG RIP

But let's assume something very different. Let's assume that the amount of Dark Energy in each cubic metre increases with time. This gives us a very different scenario – the Big Rip.

Under this scenario, "everything" gets torn apart by the increasing amounts of Dark Energy about 50 to 100 billion years in the future. This will be the End of Everything.

About 200 million years before the End, the stars in our galaxy get ripped apart from each other and fly off into empty space. One year before the End, the planets in our Solar System get flung into empty space. One hour before the End, the atoms that make up our planet explode away from each other. One tenth of a billionth of a billionth of a second before the End, electrons get ripped away from the central nucleus in their atom. And at one ten-thousandth of a billion of a billionth of a second before the End, the actual protons and neutrons in the nuclei of atoms get torn away from each other – and then the protons and neutrons disintegrate into their component quarks.

Darth Vader in the *Star Wars* saga got it wrong. It's not the Force that controls the Universe – it's Dark Energy.

Dark Energy and Gravity

Isaac Newton was such a genius that he was able to realise there was something called "Gravity" – and he worked out mathematically how Gravity pulled stuff, and that it pervaded the Entire Universe.

Albert Einstein was such a genius that he was able to realise that "Gravity" warped the Universe. To quote John A. Wheeler: "Matter curves Space–Time. Curved Space–Time tells matter how to move." (For example, the Sun curves local Space–Time in our Solar System. As a result, comets fall towards the Sun.)

Dark Energy gives us a new slant on this strange thing called "Gravity". Gravity has many "aspects" or "faces" – and one of them, Dark Energy, pushes stuff apart.

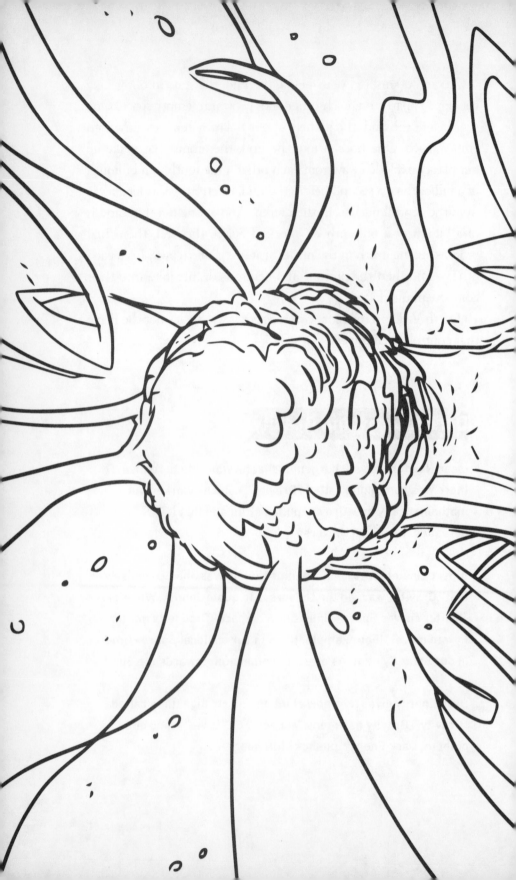

Einstein's Single Idea

Einstein would sometimes say that he had only one original
and deep thought in his whole life – and that everything
else he did came from this one single thought.

Suppose you are in a box (say, an elevator car), located
anywhere in the Universe. You weigh (say) 70 kilograms, and
you are standing on a set of scales that register 70 kilograms.
There are two scenarios.

You could be on the surface of our planet. Or you could be in
deep space in a rocket accelerating at 1G. Einstein realised
the two scenarios are identical, and that there is no test
(involving physical experiments) that you can do to
tell you in which situation you are.

From this thought came all of his Great Works.

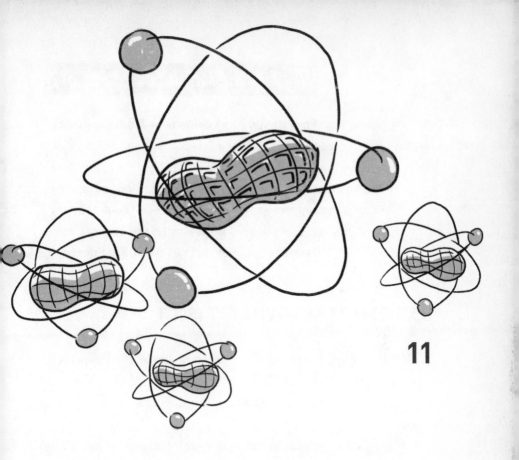

11

DARK MATTER

For almost a century, astronomers have realised that we have a major problem. It's a very basic, fundamental and simple problem.

Most of the Universe is "missing".

We actually know that it's there. The problem is that we can't see it.

We have many different types of telescopes, covering lots of the Electromagnetic Spectrum – radio, microwave, infra-red, visible light, ultraviolet, X-ray, gamma ray, and so on. But all the "stuff" astronomers find adds up to only about 5 per cent of the mass of the Universe.

What is the Universe Made of?

The latest figures come to us from the Planck Observatory, a Space Telescope launched in 2009.

It tells us that the Universe is about 13.8 billion years old – and that the Universe contains about 4.9 per cent ordinary matter, 26.8 per cent Dark Matter and 68.3 per cent Dark Energy. (See page 81 for "Dark Energy".)

DARK MATTER – WHAT IT ISN'T

So let me give you a sense of where we stand in the Big Picture. Our Universe is dominated by Dark Energy and Dark Matter. You and I are made of stuff that, in percentage terms, is close to a Rounding Error.

Only about 5 per cent of the mass of the Universe is made from "normal" matter. Humans and plants, stars and planets, belly button fluff and peanuts, and the stuff between the stars – all this is made up of regular matter based on atoms, such as protons, neutrons and electrons.

But we are quite confident that Dark Matter is not made from atoms. Furthermore, it's not made up of Black Holes, nor of stars that have died and no longer shine, nor of planets that have been thrown out of their host solar systems.

Dark Matter is made up of something strange that we currently don't understand. For example, it doesn't seem to radiate or interact with any kind of electromagnetic radiation at all. This is very different from stars that emit light, and from humans who both reflect light and absorb it (ask someone with a sunburn). That is why we can't directly "see" this mysterious Missing Mass of the Universe, Dark Matter.

In a sense, Dark Matter is like the wind. We can't see the wind directly, but we can see what the wind does. So when we see the leaves on trees fluttering and the branches bending, we know that there's some wind, even if we can't see it. In the same way, we can "see" what Dark Matter does.

Dark Matter interacts via gravity, even if it doesn't interact with electromagnetic radiation.

As a result, Dark Matter has mass, so it "makes" its own gravity. Furthermore, Dark Matter is affected by the gravity from other objects. This attraction goes both ways. Dark Matter pulls on both Regular and Dark Matter. And it can be attracted by the gravity of Regular Matter and other Dark Matter.

Why "Dark"?

Why do we call this mysterious stuff "Dark" Matter?
For the same reason that the early cartographers would inscribe "Here Be Lions" on unexplored areas of the maps they drew. They knew something was there, but had no idea what it was.

In the same way, we are very sure that something is making up a lot of our Universe, but we have no solid evidence for what kind of stuff Dark Matter is.

So the very name "Dark" is a measure of our current ignorance.

EVIDENCE FOR DARK MATTER

The astronomers have suspected the existence of Dark Matter since the 1930s. The clue was the "abnormal" orbiting of galaxies.

There are two types of orbiting. First, there's the orbiting of galaxies around each other. Second, there's the orbiting of stars within a galaxy.

Let's first look at galaxies orbiting around each other. (Actually, a bunch of galaxies in a cluster don't neatly "orbit" around each other – it's more buzzing around like angry bees.)

Way back in 1933, the astronomer Fritz Zwicky took a very close look at a cluster (or group) of galaxies called the Coma Cluster. He measured the speeds of the individual galaxies inside this cluster. He found, to his vast surprise, that they were going so fast that based on what his telescopes showed him, they should easily break away from the gravity of this cluster of galaxies.

But the individual galaxies were not breaking away from the others.

Zwicky worked out that to keep the Coma Cluster intact and stable, there had to be at least 10 to 20 times more matter in the Coma Cluster than he could see with his telescopes. This was one of the first hints of the existence of Dark Matter.

Scientific Insult

It was Zwicky who invented the phrase "spherical bastard" to describe people whom he thought were obnoxious. No matter which way you looked at them, they were still a "bastard".

MORE EVIDENCE FOR DARK MATTER

So what about the second clue, the speeds at which stars orbit inside a galaxy?

In 1973 the astronomer Vera Rubin was one of the first to discover this particular anomaly. In her research, she would pick a galaxy, typically one with about 100 billion stars in it. Then, using a new technology of the time, she measured how fast the stars were orbiting around the centre of that galaxy. She got a real surprise.

It turns out that the orbiting of stars inside a galaxy is nothing like the orbiting of planets inside our Solar System.

In our Solar System, the planets close to the Sun orbit around really rapidly, while the planets further out from the Sun travel much more slowly. So the innermost planet, Mercury, whizzes at around 48 kilometres per second, our Earth travels a little slower at 30 kilometres per second, while Neptune way out

> It turns out that the orbiting of stars inside a galaxy is nothing like the orbiting of planets inside our Solar System.

on the edge crawls along at around 5.4 kilometres per second.

But that was not what Rubin saw in galaxies. The stars near the bulging core of a galaxy travel around at roughly the same speed as the stars right out on the edge. In our Milky Way, there's literally and figuratively a whole galaxy of stars – some are close to the central Black Hole, while others are 50,000 light years away from it (way out on the edge). Amazingly, they all travel at roughly the same speed – about 210 to 250 kilometres per second.

There was only one way that the theoretical astronomers could explain how a galaxy could spin like this. The maths told them that the galaxy had to be surrounded by a halo, or spherical ball, of some type of matter. And, because they couldn't see this mysterious matter, they called it "Dark Matter".

DARK MATTER SHAPED OUR UNIVERSE

As a result of its gravity, Dark Matter has another strange property: it seems to be the invisible scaffolding that formed stars and galaxies. That's right, Dark Matter shaped our current Universe. In fact, it completely controlled the arrangement of our superclusters of galaxies – and the stars and the gas in between just went along for the ride.

> **Dark Matter completely controlled the arrangement of our superclusters of galaxies – and the stars and the gas in between just went along for the ride.**

After the Big Bang, the Universe was very bright and smooth for about 100 million years. There was lots of Dark Matter back then, probably making up about half of the mass or energy of the Universe.

This Dark Matter had mass, and so it had gravity. It then coalesced under its own gravity, and began to form structures built out of Dark Matter. The gravity of these Dark Matter structures attracted Regular Matter, such as atoms of hydrogen, helium and lithium. These condensed and formed into stars in big clumps of early "proto-galaxies" – which then formed into galaxies.

So Dark Matter set up the original arrangements of matter in the Universe, with the much smaller amounts of Regular Matter just along for the ride.

This pattern persists in today's Universe.

The Early Days

Back in the Early Days, when the Universe had cooled down enough for atoms and the like to come into existence, the stuff that made up the Universe existed in quite different ratios.

Atoms made up 12 per cent of the early Universe (currently about 5 per cent), Dark Matter made up 63 per cent (currently about 27 per cent), Photons made up 15 per cent and Neutrinos 10 per cent.

DARK MATTER SHAPED OUR MILKY WAY

The shape of our Milky Way is dominated by the invisible Dark Matter, which makes up about 80 to 90 per cent of the mass of our galaxy (about 10 to 20 times as much as Regular Matter). Dark Matter provides the gravitational "glue" that gives our galaxy its shape.

Dwarf galaxies are dominated by Dark Matter, usually having 100 times as much of it as Regular Matter. Segue 1, a dwarf galaxy that hangs out on the edges of our Milky Way galaxy, is an extreme case – it has about 1000 times as much Dark Matter as Regular Matter. But other structures associated with our Milky Way, such as Globular Clusters of stars, have virtually no Dark Matter.

It seems that Dark Matter is not evenly spread throughout our Milky Way. It also seems that a few galaxies have very little, if any, Dark Matter.

We don't yet know why.

DARK MATTER – WHAT WE KNOW

So what do we know about this Dark Matter?

First, it's dark because it doesn't directly interact with visible light, or indeed any electromagnetic radiation. Dark Matter is not burnt-out stars, planets or gas.

Second, it's definitely not Regular Matter, like the stuff you and I are made of. The astronomers can tell us this from their observations of various galaxies colliding, and of star clusters colliding.

Third, Dark Matter is not antimatter. If it were, we would see very specific and characteristic gamma rays being produced whenever Dark Matter collided with Regular Matter.

Fourth, we know that it's not Black Holes. Black Holes have a lot of mass crammed into a small volume, so they have a very strong local gravitational field. If they were involved we would expect to see lots of Gravitational Lenses, where gravity bends the light of a distant object. We're simply not seeing those.

Fifth, astronomers have mapped Dark Matter on a huge scale, analysing the light from 10 million galaxies. These galaxies are typically some six billion light years away. The astronomers analysed this incoming light to see how it was curved or bent – presumably by intervening Dark Matter. After five years of hard work, they mapped an intricate cosmic mesh of intermingled visible galaxies and invisible Dark Matter. This mesh covers many billions of light years.

The Dark Matter seems to be arranged like a giant sponge – with dense and empty regions.

Another way to visualise it is to think of the Universe as a giant web, with long filaments of Dark Matter. And wherever these vast filaments connect with each other, we can usually see giant clusters of galaxies. However, we can't directly see the long filaments of Dark Matter. But we know that they are there, because the enormous mass of this invisible Dark Matter bends and distorts the light of regular visible galaxies in the background behind them.

WHAT IS DARK MATTER?

There are three main contenders for the title of Dark Matter at the moment, each of them exotic and strange.

The main categories are Hot Dark Matter, Warm Dark Matter and Cold Dark Matter. "Hot" means that the particles that make it up have lots of energy in their velocity, "Warm" that they have less, and "Cold" even less again. At the moment, Cold Dark Matter is very popular, that is, slow-moving exotic particles such as certain kinds of WIMPs or Weakly Interacting Massive Particles (which can also be "warm" or "hot"), but that could change. There are various theoretical reasons why Cold Dark Matter is currently the best choice – and there are very few actual findings that, tantalisingly, can be interpreted as suggesting a candidate.

And if Dark Matter does turn out to be Cold, then this will be a case when the WIMPs won . . .

Gravitational Lenses

Dark Matter can indirectly interact with light.

Anything that has mass automatically has gravity.
This gravity bends light.

So a gravitational field between us and a more distant
source of light will bend that light. This is called Gravitational
Lensing. Einstein predicted this, but thought that it was
purely a theoretical concept. However, it turns out to be
an effect that we can see with our telescopes.

This is how Dark Matter can affect light – indirectly.
Dark Matter has mass, which means that it has its
own gravity. This gravity can then bend the path of
any light that happens to pass near the Dark Matter.

12

DRINKING GLASS SHAPES PERCEPTION

The hippies used to say that "Reality is for people who can't handle drugs". But reality is hard to perceive, let alone handle. This is especially the case with the concept of "volume". Apparently, even if two glasses have the same volume, we "see" the taller glass as having more volume. So we think that the shorter, wider glass has less volume, and drink it more quickly.

ALCOHOL AND HEALTH

It seems quite possible that drinking small amounts of alcohol can be good for your health.

But Binge Drinking is a different schooner of fish.

It's well and truly linked to an increase in criminal activity. But that's not all.

Binge Drinking is also a health hazard. Two and a half million people die each year as a result of drinking too much alcohol, according to the World Health Organization. In fact, dangerous levels of alcohol consumption cause about 4 per cent of all disease worldwide.

It seems to be a hard job to get people to reduce their alcohol intake. But at least we can help them estimate how much they are actually drinking. Unfortunately, it's too easy to fool our senses. Even minor factors such as drinking from a beer glass with curved sides means that you will drink more quickly than if the beer glass has straight sides.

But first things first.

POUR INTO GLASS?

Before you can drink from a glass, you need to pour alcohol into that glass. We humans can't even do that consistently.

Say that you are asked to pour a standard shot of alcohol into a straight-sided glass – just by eye, without using a measure. A study by Dr Brian Wansink from Cornell University in the USA gave this simple job to 198 students and 86 professional bartenders.

The students poured 30 per cent more alcohol into a short, wide glass than into a tall, narrow glass. (You might not be surprised by this.) The students said that they thought the tall glass had a greater volume, so they were deliberately compensating for this when they poured alcohol in the short, wide glass.

Interestingly, professional bartenders, with an average of over 6.3 years of bartending experience, were only a little better. They poured 20 per cent more alcohol into the short, wide glass than into the tall, narrow glass.

In plain English, when you pour alcoholic drinks (measuring by eye) into a short, wide glass, your estimate of two drinks is actually equal to about two-and-a-half standard drinks.

Should people drink alcohol only from tall, narrow glasses?

> Should people drink alcohol only from tall, narrow glasses? Or, should we drink always from glasses that have volume levels marked on them?

Or, should we drink always from glasses that have volume levels marked on them? If you are happy with Function over Form, you could inscribe your own level marks on each of your glasses with a diamond ring.

DRINK FROM GLASS

Let's move past pouring – what about getting to drink the alcohol from a glass? Well, the first thing to realise is that there are many types of glasses.

As an aside, there has been a recent increase in glasses that have curved shapes and also have ads on them. The brands marketing this way include Stella Artois, Heineken, Guinness, Smirnoff, Carlsberg and Jameson. The curvy glasses might be chalices, curved beer flutes, tankards or novelty-shaped beer glasses.

These curvy glasses have two functions. First, they conspicuously promote the brand. And second, they disguise the true volume of the beverage. Because so many of these glasses curve outwards from a narrow base, most of the volume of the alcoholic drink is carried in the upper part of the glass. We know that people are easily tricked and when they are trying to judge the volume of an object, they often simply relate it directly to the height.

So if you take a sip from one of these curved glasses, the level won't drop much and you'll think that you haven't consumed much.

It's not just Beauty that's in the Eye of the Beer-Holder – it's also the volume of the glass.

One study by Dr Angela Attwood and colleagues from the University of Bristol in the United Kingdom recruited 159 social alcohol drinkers – half male and half female – to study this phenomenon. They had two different types of glasses. One had straight and parallel sides – so the halfway level in height was the same as the halfway point in volume. But the other glass had curved sides that swelled outwards from a narrow base. In this case, the midpoint for height was quite different from the midpoint for volume.

The results were interesting. If the sides curved outwards, the punters would scull their 350 millilitres of lager in about seven minutes. But when they drank from the glass with straight sides, they drank more slowly – and took about 11 minutes to finish the same volume. Whatever the shape the glass was, they took roughly the same number of sips of alcohol – and each sip took roughly the same time. The main difference was that with a straight glass they spent more time having a rest in between sips.

So what's going on?

SOCIOLOGY OF VOLUME

We drink more slowly from a tall, narrow glass than from a curved glass – and we don't really know why. But, surely, if we can pace ourselves better when drinking from a tall, narrow glass with straight sides, wouldn't that be a good choice?

Another Volume issue is that "pubs have started serving drinks in larger glasses and offering cheap promotions to encourage people to drink more", according to Moira Plant, Professor of Alcohol Studies at the University of the West of England.

It seems that it's not just Beauty that's in the Eye of the Beer-Holder – it's also the volume of the glass. So next time you're pouring a drink at home, don't be half-hearted and take half measures to estimate the volume – measure it accurately . . .

13

DVD ©OPYRIGHT THEFT

If you have bought or rented a movie sometime in the last few years, you would have had to sit through the compulsory Anti-Piracy video at the beginning. You know, the one with the urgent Death Metal Thrash Techno music in the background, and the words on the screen telling you that you wouldn't steal a car, or a handbag, or a television. It then goes on to tell you that "downloading pirated movies is stealing" and furthermore that "stealing is against the law" and finishes off with the bleak message that "piracy is a crime".

It sounds very reasonable that authors should be reimbursed for their hard work.

But here's an interesting question: that insistent, driving music that runs all the way through the well-known Anti-Piracy ad – was it paid for? The inconvenient answer is that it was stolen.

COLLECTING MUSIC ROYALTIES – THEORY

Most countries have some kind of agency to collect royalties relating to music. That agency monitors radio, TV and movies to make sure that musicians get paid when the music that they wrote gets played. In the Netherlands, the music royalty collection agency is called Buma/Stemra.

Back in 2006, a Dutch coalition involved in the film industry, called Filmwereld, approached a Dutch musician, Melchior Reitveldt, to write some music for an Anti-Piracy ad. The offer came with the strict proviso that this music would be played only at a local film festival.

Reitveldt wrote the music, it was played at the film festival, he got paid and all was well.

But then, in 2007, he bought a Harry Potter DVD. To his surprise, there was his music in the Anti-Piracy ad at the beginning. His composition had been taken and used without his permission. In fact, it had been illegally used on over ten million Dutch DVDs, as well as overseas. You might have one at home right now.

COLLECTING MUSIC ROYALTIES – PRACTICE

So Reitveldt approached the Buma/Stemra royalty collection agency to clear up this misunderstanding, and ran into a brick wall. Nothing happened for a long time, and then pathetically small payments were offered but not paid in full, lists of DVDs that carried his music were promised but not delivered – the delays went on and on.

Finally, in 2011, about half a decade after the original theft of his music, there was a very strange "breakthrough".

Allegedly, one of the directors of Buma/Stemra, Mr Jochem Gerrits, spoke to Reitveldt's financial adviser personally, offering to speed things up. Gerrits made a simple offer: everything would proceed nicely if the musician, Reitveldt, would simply

> That insistent, driving music that runs all the way through the well-known Anti-Piracy ad – was it paid for? The inconvenient answer is that it was stolen.

sell the contested piece of music to him, Gerrits (more specifically, to Gerrits's music publishing company, High Fashion Music). Buma/Stemra would then make a payout of one million euros and Gerrits would keep one third for all his trouble and hard work, and the musician, Reitveldt, would keep two thirds.

It's a bit like if you report your stolen property to the police, and after a lot of dilly-dallying, a very senior police officer approaches you offering to give two thirds of your property back to you, if you give them one third.

Luckily, the conversation was recorded and Reitveldt went to the media. Gerrits resigned from the board of the Buma/Stemra music royalty collection agency. In June 2012, the court ordered Buma/Stemra to make some repayments.

WHAT DO YOU OWN?

Today, in the new world of the Interweb, copyright is complicated. In the old days, if you bought a book you could give or lend it to a friend. But it's different today with the modern "electronic versions" of books.

A woman in Duluth, Minnesota, did the modern equivalent of lending an album to friends. She shared 24 songs that had a total retail value of US$23.76. The Recording Industry Association of America sued her, and the court awarded it US$222,000.

In terms of the Multiplication Factor, that has to be a runaway, chart-busting, solid-gold smash hit . . .

History of Copyright

The concepts of "copyright" and "intellectual property"
didn't really take hold in Asia because of its many different
cultures, economics, legal structures and societies.
In Europe, there was no real concept of "literary
property" until the rise of early capitalism.

Protection of literary property probably began in Great
Britain in 1710, with the so-called "British Statute of Queen
Anne". This Statute opened with the description that it was:
"An Act for the Encouragement of Learning, by Vesting the
Copies of Printed Books in the Authors." It then pointed
out that, rather naughtily, "Printers, Booksellers and Other
Persons have of late frequently taken the Liberty of Printing
. . . Books, and other Writings, without the Consent of the
Authors." As you would expect, this nefarious act led to
the poor authors' "very great Detriment, (and) too often
to the Ruin of them and their Families".

This early concept led to our current situation of "copyright".
With the rise of the Internet, and Internet Publishing, it
seems that there will be more new concepts to come.

EIGHT GLASSES OF WATER PER DAY

You see them everywhere. Those ubiquitous plastic bottles of water have become absolutely essential to some people's lives. Do they believe that this bottled water is life-giving, and that without it they would spontaneously dehydrate and die?

This water fixation might be a response to the constant and incorrect background rumble to "drink at least eight glasses of water a day".

This "eight glasses per day" advice has been published in reputable-seeming publications, including a health column in the *New York Times*, and also by many well-meaning writers in the popular press. It even appears in a pamphlet from the University of California, Los Angeles, which advises the students to "carry a water bottle with you. Drink often while sitting in class . . ." And, of course, this incorrect information pops up intermittently in your email inbox.

HISTORY OF THE MYTH

Back in 1995, Fereydoon Batmanghelidj, an Iranian-born physician living in the USA, wrote the book *Your Body's Many Cries for Water*.

In it, he claimed that conditions such as arthritis, angina, migraine, back pain, headache, high blood pressure, ulcers and even asthma were all caused by people foolishly not drinking enough water. He proposed that people "need to learn they're not sick, only thirsty".

Many of his incorrect claims appear in the scary emails. But it turns out that the falsehoods go back even further.

Water Myths = Fluid Lies

73 per cent of Americans are chronically dehydrated.

If you are thirsty, it's too late – you are already dehydrated.

In 37 per cent of Americans, the thirst mechanism is so weak that it is often mistaken for hunger.

Water is a tonic for the skin.

Water flushes out fat.

EXPOSING THE MYTH

Professor Henry Valtin, from the Department of Physiology at Dartmouth Medical School in New Hampshire, decided to look for any scientific evidence supporting the drinking of eight glasses of water each day. He searched very widely through the peer-reviewed literature in modern electronic databases, as well as in the older printed literature. He also consulted with nutritionists who specialised in the fields of thirst and the drinking of fluids.

In all of this research, he found no evidence to support the drinking of eight glasses of water per day.

But he did manage to track down how some sensible advice got misquoted.

Back in 1945, the US Food and Nutrition Board of the National Research Council wrote, "a suitable allowance for adults is 2.5 liters daily in most instances . . . Most of this quantity is contained in prepared foods."

That's right, most of the water you need is already there in the food you eat. It seems that the important last part – "most of this quantity is contained in prepared foods" – just got ignored.

WATER NUMBERS

Each day, a healthy adult human in a temperate climate will typically take some two and a half litres of water into their body, and then pass it out again. (You will need more water if you are on a long-haul jet flight, or have a fever, or have kidney stones, or are working hard or are sweating – that is, in special circumstances. You get the picture.)

Most of the time, this liquid you take in will be made up of about 1220 millilitres of water in some kind of fluid, and another 1000 millilitres of water contained in your food. Inside your body, you "manufacture" another 300 millilitres of water per day, known as "metabolic water". So that works out to 2520 millilitres of water available to your body.

Then you lose about 1520 millilitres of water in your urine, and another 100 millilitres in your faeces. And when you add in another 900 millilitres for so-called "insensible" losses (water that is lost through sweating or breathing) you get a total output of 2520 millilitres of water.

So about 1200 millilitres as a drink of some kind of fluid is all you need to maintain your water balance – if you're a normal adult, in a temperate climate, leading a mostly sedentary lifestyle.

A fundamental assumed belief of the "eight glasses of water per day" story is that many of us are chronically dehydrated, and are not sensitive enough or sufficiently tuned into our bodies to correct this by being thirsty. From a physiological point of view, this is rubbish.

Beer Thirst

Diuretics make you manufacture and pass more urine. Alcohol is a diuretic and so can make you thirsty.

For example, drinking 200 millilitres of regular beer will have you urinating 320 millilitres. The alcohol acts directly on hormone production in your brain.

Luckily, when you drink alcohol you get thirsty, and you automatically drink more water. But there might be a little delay before you correct your water balance.

THIRST 101

Thirst is the desire to drink, usually caused by a lack in fluids, or by an increase in the "saltiness" (osmolality) of your body fluids. You regulate the osmolality of your body fluids within the very narrow range of 280 to 296 milliosmols per kilogram of water (H_2O). This is mostly done by receptors (for osmolality and volume) and hormones (for example, vasopressin). In response to a change in osmolality or volume of your bodily fluids, you change how much you drink or how much urine you make.

> About 1200 millilitres as a drink of some kind of fluid is all you need to maintain your water balance if you're a normal adult leading a mostly sedentary lifestyle.

The sensation of thirst as a trigger to drink liquid is sensitive enough, accurate enough and quick enough to keep the composition of your bodily fluids within the normal range. (However, it can be fooled or overridden by extreme conditions, such as running a marathon on a very hot day.)

Our brain and kidneys work tightly to regulate our osmolality on a minute-by-minute basis. With regard to dehydration or "drying out", the whole system (receptors and hormones) begins to make major adjustments at around 284.7 milliosmols per kilogram of H_2O. This is long before we consciously feel the sensation of thirst.

The sensation of thirst arises into our consciousness when plasma osmolality is around 294 milliosmols per kilogram of H_2O and rising. This is still within the normal range, and a long way from dehydration, which most experts consider begins at around 302 milliosmols per kilogram of H_2O.

Very, very rarely, the sensation of thirst won't make you drink. This can happen if your osmo-receptors are damaged (Adipsic Hypernatraemia Syndrome) or because the Set Point of osmolality in the brain has been shifted.

But, overwhelmingly, if you drink water when you are thirsty, your osmolality will remain within the normal range.

TAKE-HOME MESSAGE

The specialists who know a lot about the in-and-out of water around the body are the nephrologists – kidney specialists. A typical opinion is that of Dr Jürgen Schnermann, a kidney physiologist at the US National Institutes of Health. He reckons that "to replace daily losses of water, an average-sized adult with healthy kidneys sitting in a temperate climate needs no more than one litre of fluid".

Drinking eight glasses of water per day is more than you need, but most people can handle this simply with extra urination.

Drink Too Much?

Usually, there is nothing wrong with drinking lots of water.

However, excessive amounts of water can be fatal.

In January 2007, a mother of three, Jennifer Strange, entered a contest run by the Sacramento, California, radio station KDND. The person who could drink the most water without going to the toilet would win a Nintendo Wii game console. The competition was called "Hold your Wee for a Wii". She drank about 7.5 litres of water, suffered severe swelling of the brain and died.

In a few hours she drank three times as much as she normally took in over a whole day.

On the other hand, consider the benefits of drinking plain water – as opposed to constant soft drinks, fruit juices, and tea and coffee. Let me emphasise that I mean tap water, not bottled water. Some studies showed that drinking lots of water reduced the incidence of cancer of the bladder, colorectal cancer, premalignant adenomatous polyps, urinary tract infections and urinary stones. Other studies showed lower risk of fatal heart disease.

It shouldn't be this hard to get it right. As the Harvard Men's Health Watch wrote, "it's getting to be quite a chore: tracking grams of fat and fiber, adding milligrams of sodium, counting calories, and now watching water".

What is the next stage? Will parents send their children off to school with the anxious advice, "Now, make sure you breathe enough air"?

Stupid Plastic Bottles

Bottled water costs more than petrol! It costs up to 10,000 times more than tap water.

It takes lots of greenhouse gases to produce, transport, store and refrigerate individual bottles of water. To make enough PET (polyethylene terephthalate) for one year's supply of plastic bottles for Australia takes over 300,000 barrels of oil. To make a tonne of PET releases three tonnes of carbon dioxide.

It is perfectly true that PET bottles can be recycled – but 63 per cent are not. They make up about one third of all roadside litter.

In my home, we use stainless steel bottles and refill them from the tap.

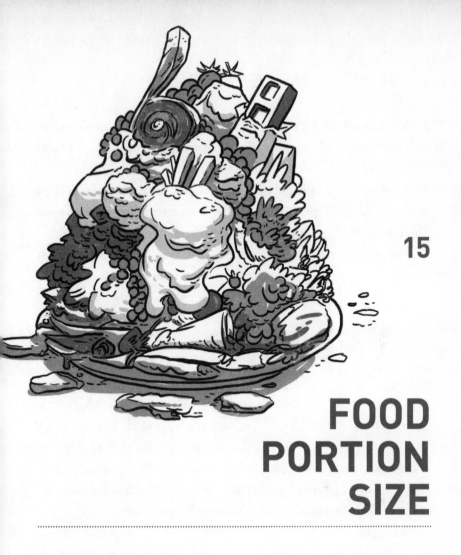

FOOD PORTION SIZE

We humans have been around for hundreds of thousands of years. For most of that time, food has been hard to get – so if we found some, we ate it, even if we weren't hungry. We've had a relatively stable food supply (thanks to agriculture) for only about 10,000 years – a very short time compared to hundreds of thousands of years.

As a result, lots of people have weird relationships with food.

Welcome to the famous Portion Size Effect. The more that's on your plate, the more you eat. It doesn't matter how hungry you are, or your gender, or how fat or thin you are – the more there is, the more you eat.

FOOD PORTION SIZE EFFECT

In one typical study, people were offered a macaroni and cheese dish for their lunch. It came in various weights – 500, 625, 750 and 1000 grams.

Surprisingly, people did not eat until they were satisfied and then stop. No. Instead, people ate 30 per cent more food if they were offered the 1000-gram portion as compared to 500 grams.

You also see the Portion Size Effect at the movies. People stuff themselves more when their portion of popcorn or candy is larger – regardless of how hungry they actually are.

> Over the past few decades, the portion sizes of foods have increased sharply in supermarkets, restaurants and fast-food establishments.

It happens if the food has no real shape (macaroni and cheese) or if it's well defined (a sandwich). It happens with foods low in energy density (soups, fruit) and high in energy density (heavy pasta bakes or fried food). It happens with packaged snacks, unpackaged snacks or just regular meals on a plate. It happens if you eat alone or with friends in a group.

It happens with people aged five and up – but not with children about three years old or under. (I guess it takes a few years to teach kids to Clean Their Plate – whether they're hungry or not).

PORTIONS GROW

The way we eat in the Western World has changed a lot over the past few generations.

People increasingly eat food outside the family home. Take-away food is convenient, relatively cheap, highly palatable and (you guessed it) provided in large portions.

In fact, over the past few decades, the portion sizes of foods have increased sharply across the board – in supermarkets, restaurants and fast-food establishments.

HOW WE EAT

Strangely, most of us are unaware of what is an "appropriate" portion of food. We mostly don't know how much we should eat to provide us with all the energy and nutrients that we need.

Instead, we usually eat either a constant volume or a constant weight of food. This is independent of whether the food is a low-energy density soup, or something really loaded with calories or kilojoules, such as peanut butter, or a hamburger with cheese and bacon.

IRRATIONAL

There are a whole bunch of irrational factors involved with the Portion Size Effect.

First, most of us are not consciously aware of the sizes of food portions that we eat. Mind you, we do think that we are getting better value for money if we get the larger portions.

Second, we eat more when the same sized portion is served in a larger bowl than when it is served in a smaller bowl.

Third, if we are eating ice-cream, we will eat more if we use a larger spoon than if we use a smaller spoon.

So it seems that we humans use various visual shortcuts when we eat. When you combine these two factors – that we underestimate large portion sizes and that we usually don't know how much energy we need to consume – then we are likely to find ourselves overeating.

Other studies altered the size of the food portions by a factor of two to one. But the volunteers who ate the food didn't notice.

First, the more you eat, the less pleasant and enjoyable each mouthful becomes. And second, whether you eat a big portion or a little portion, your feelings of hunger and fullness are the same at the end of eating.

We know that the Portion Size Effect is real – but it's poorly understood. Sensory Influences (such as what you see or smell) are part of it. Cognitive Factors (such as what your parents taught you, the norms of society around you, financial considerations, and so on) are another part.

One puzzling aspect is the so-called Post-Ingestive Consequences – what happens after you've eaten the meal? Here are a few weird findings.

First, the more you eat, the less pleasant and enjoyable each mouthful becomes. And second, whether you eat a big portion or a little portion, your feelings of hunger and fullness are the same at the end of eating.

But regardless of "enjoyment" and "fullness", we still keep on eating. Why?

OVERCOMING AN EVOLUTIONARY HICCUP

There is an advantage to consciously understanding that the Portion Size Effect exists. This knowledge can help us deal with this evolutionary hangover from our distant past, that is, the urge to stuff ourselves because food was usually scarce.

The first thing to realise is that we can control how much we designate to be a "portion". We can serve ourselves smaller portions when eating at home. In a restaurant, we can ask for a smaller portion. Or if we get a portion that is too large, we can simply divide it in half, eat only one half and take the remainder home for later. In fact, the more often we eat in restaurants, the more we eat and the fatter we get – so eat more often at home.

There's another way to take advantage of the Portion Size Effect. Remember that it also applies to foods that some people don't find particularly palatable, such as vegetables (although, personally, I do love my veggies, especially a slightly browned and crispy eggplant).

So serving kids large portions of veggies might trick them into eating more of what's good for them, which is a good thing – because you are teaching them good taste.

FREE WILL

The concept of "Free Will" is something that philosophers have been worrying about for thousands of years. "Free Will" is our ability to make a choice. For example, you might suddenly decide to walk to work rather than take the bus because the Sun feels so nice on your face.

But what if neuroscientists could tell you what your spontaneous decision was *before* you made it?

Would that mean that Free Will is an illusion? Are we making decisions, or is there a homunculus (a little man) sitting inside our brain making decisions for us, and letting us know about them later?

FREE WILL IN SOCIETY

The idea of "Free Will" has rippled through our societies for thousands of years.

On one hand, we have thinkers (the so-called "Hard Determinists"), such as Martin Luther, who reject Free Will. On the other hand, thinkers such as Thomas Reid and Robert Kane (the so-called "Metaphysical Libertarians") accept Free Will.

The Western Legal System is based on the concept that we have Free Will – and, as a result, we can be held accountable for our actions. But if there is no Free Will, are we legally to blame for our actions? And from an ethics point of view, how morally accountable are we for our actions with Free Will, as opposed to without it?

In a religious setting, both Christianity and Islam believe in a Creator who is both all-powerful and all-knowing, and therefore knows what the future will be. But each faith has a dogma that also states that the Creator allows us individually to decide to either follow the Path of Righteousness, or to reject it.

IS FREE WILL ONLY AN ILLUSION?

And finally, from a scientific point of view, what do we make of the research where neuroscientists can predict what you will do several seconds before you do it?

This research involves several similar experiments. Each experiment required that the volunteer make a decision at a time of the volunteer's choosing. In each study, the subject would look at some kind of counting device. At the exact moment they made their decision, they would remember what registered on the counting device and report it to the researchers. The researchers then knew *exactly when* the subject thought they had made the decision.

The researchers also monitored the brain activity of the volunteers. As the decades rolled by, the experiments became increasingly sophisticated. But the result was always the same. By looking at brain activity, the researcher could predict *when* the volunteer would make the decision. And in the more sophisticated later experiments, they could predict *what* that decision would be.

1970s STUDY

The original research goes back to the 1970s. Benjamin Libet from the Physiology Department at the University of California, San Francisco, got his volunteers to tap a finger whenever they happened to feel the urge to do so. It was entirely up to their Free Will as to when this would happen. (Libet was following up on similar research carried out in 1964 by the neurologists Hans Helmut Kornhuber and Lüder Deecke.) The timing device was a light racing around a clock face once every 2.56 seconds. The volunteer would remember where the light was at the moment they made their decision.

> The Western Legal System is based on the concept that we have Free Will – and, as a result, we can be held accountable for our actions.

The volunteers had a hat made out of a net of electroencephalograph (EEG) electrodes placed on their heads to monitor brain activity. Libet detected a spike in electrical activity about half a second before the volunteers decided to tap a finger.

One problem with this research is that tapping a finger is a gross motor activity, not a higher-level intellectual activity. Another problem is that trying to sense the more subtle activity of the brain by what you pick up with electrodes on the skin is pretty crude. It's like listening to a recording of a concert and trying to work out what colour shoes the singer is wearing.

My Brain Cancer Made Me Do It

In 1966, Charles Whitman carried a shotgun, handguns and rifles to the top of the University Tower in Austin, Texas. Over the next hour and a half, he killed 13 people and wounded 32 more. He was then fatally shot by a policeman who forced his way to the top of the Tower.

Before this event, Whitman had seen a doctor who wrote in his notes, "[Whitman] initiated [the session] with the statement that something seemed to be happening to him, and that he didn't seem to be himself." In a note he wrote before his death, Whitman asked that an autopsy be carried out on his body. It turned out that the autopsy found a brain cancer – an astrocytoma – pressing on his amygdala.

Does that mean that Whitman was to blame for what he did, or did the brain cancer make him do it?

2008 EXPERIMENT

A follow-up paper by Dr Chun Siong Soon and colleagues in 2008 went a little further.

They got their volunteers to carry out a "freely paced motor-decision task" while their brain activity was being measured using functional Magnetic Resonance Imaging (fMRI). The scanner looked at the metabolic activity of various parts of the volunteers' brains. For timing purposes, the researchers showed letters of the alphabet to volunteers at half-second intervals.

They also asked their volunteers to press one of two buttons at any time they felt like it. The subjects could decide both when to push, and whether to use the left or right hand. They quoted which letter was on the screen when they made the decision – and this gave the researchers the timing of the decision.

By looking at the brain waves, the researchers could predict what choices the volunteers would make up to 10 seconds in advance.

However, the researchers were still testing motor activity – movement of the hands.

2013 EXPERIMENT

The latest research by Dr Soon and colleagues again monitored brain activity by testing the volunteers inside an fMRI scanner. But this time, the volunteers had a more intellectual task.

They were shown images at the rate of one per second. Each image had a number in the centre of the image. Using their Free Will, the volunteers had two decisions to make.

The first decision was to decide *when* to start doing arithmetic with these numbers. The second decision was *whether* to add the number on one image and, one second later, the next image – or whether they would subtract them.

Amazingly, by looking at the fMRI scans, the neuroscientists could predict *when* the volunteers would make a decision, and *whether* they would do an addition or a subtraction. And, even more amazingly, they could make this prediction up to four seconds before the volunteers were aware of their own decisions.

Interestingly, different parts of the brain were involved. The regions of the brain that predicted *when* the volunteers would make the decision were quite different from the regions that predicted *whether* the arithmetic would be addition or subtraction.

It is curious that a mental calculation (in the 2013 experiment) had less predictive time than the simpler left-or-right hand choice (2008 experiment). I wonder what this means?

WILL WE EVER KNOW?

This line of research is a step in trying to understand the ancient problem of whether Free Will exists and, if it does, how to define what it is. It will be a long time before we solve this problem – if we ever do.

After all, if the human brain was simple enough for us to understand, we wouldn't be smart enough to figure it out . . .

The Brain is not the Mind

There are problems with using sophisticated scanners to monitor the brain. They all relate to our brain.

First, the same regions of the brain handle many different tasks. The amygdala is involved with fear. But it also lights up during happiness, anger, novelty and sexual arousal (at least, in women). The insula is involved in insight. But it is also involved in empathy, aversion and processing trust.

Second, the same event can set off many different patterns of firing in your brain. You may order a salad, but your brain activity will be different if you are tired or alert, drunk or sober. Furthermore, different brain states may trigger the same reaction, for example, being tired or hungry can make you get a glass of water.

Third, the same object can have different meanings. A glass of water can be part of a casual social interchange, or it can be lifesaving to somebody dying of thirst.

I Am

French philosopher, mathematician and author
René Descartes famously said, "I think, therefore I am."

The motto of the Scientist is, "I think, therefore I get paid."

FUNCTIONAL FOOD

Next time you go shopping for food in the supermarket, check out the wording on the packets. The claims they make are very impressive – and especially appealing to anybody who likes to keep healthy and strong.

Both breakfast cereals and the various vitamin-enriched waters will allegedly improve your kid's immune system, while carrots will supposedly improve your eyesight. Grape juice is purported to improve your heart, while yoghurt will evidently coddle your colon.

Welcome to the New World of "Functional Foods", or "Foods with Benefits". Unfortunately, most of their health claims are unproven.

Real Functional Foods

We have indeed successfully altered a very
small number of foods to improve our health.

We've added iodine to salt to successfully reduce goitre,
and Vitamin D to milk to successfully reduce rickets. In
pregnancy, folic acid added to bread successfully reduces
the incidence of spina bifida in babies. And, yes, "calcium
supports strong bones" and, yes, "diets low in salt
may reduce the risk of high blood pressure".

In some foods, adding or subtracting
something can help improve health.

But, as Marion Nestle, a professor of Nutrition,
Food Studies and Public Health at New York University,
said of the current crop of Functional Foods: "They
are not about health. They are about marketing."

"FAKE" CLAIMS

There are a very small number of success stories where we have
altered foods to improve our health.

But these very few real successes stand apart from the misinterpretations, half-truths and outright mistruths used to advertise some
of these so-called Functional Foods. But promoting these so-called
Functional Foods is worth lots of money. In the USA, retail sales of
these foods reached US$37.3 billion in 2009.

Thanks to regulations in various countries, Big Food companies
have to be very careful *not* to claim that their product will prevent or
cure diseases. However, they do have "creative" people writing for them.

For example, in 2009, the Federal Trade Commission in the USA filed a complaint of "deceptive marketing" regarding a Kellogg's breakfast cereal called Frosted Mini-Wheats.

In a TV ad for the cereal, the voiceover explained that: "A clinical study showed kids who had a filling breakfast of Frosted Mini-Wheats cereal improved their attentiveness by 20 per cent." Sure enough, there had been a study – which Kellogg had commissioned.

> We've added iodine to salt to successfully reduce goitre, and Vitamin D to milk to successfully reduce rickets.

But the study had two major problems. First, it compared kids who ate Frosted Mini-Wheats for breakfast with kids who ate no food at all for breakfast – they were allowed only water. And second, only about half the kids who ate the Frosted Mini-Wheats had any improvement after three hours.

MORE DECEPTIVE CLAIMS

Another American example of "deceptive marketing" was the proclamation on the front of Quaker Oatmeal Squares cereal: "Oatmeal helps reduce cholesterol!"

That is correct – but only if you eat oatmeal in a very unusual way.

First, you have to eat three bowls a day, which adds up to nearly half of your total daily energy needs. Second, you have to *not* add any milk, and either eat it dry or with water only.

The same trick was used with a yoghurt called Activa. The TV ad showed "an animated diagram in which yellow dots were superimposed over a woman's abdomen. At first they all clumped together; then, as if by magic, they transformed into a yellow-dotted downward arrow". This seems to be referring to constipation, or "bowel transit time". At the same time the voiceover said, "Activa eaten every day is clinically proven to help regulate your digestive system in two weeks."

There are two problems here.

First, many of the internal scientific studies from the company that made Activa showed it was no better at reducing constipation than a placebo. Second, in the studies that did show a difference, the volunteers ate the yoghurt three times every day.

Neither of these facts was mentioned in the ads.

EVEN MORE DODGY CLAIMS

Dr Oz (full name Dr Mehmet Cengiz Oz) is a surgeon who became famous after appearing on The Oprah Winfrey Show in 2004. By 2009, he had his own daily TV show.

One episode of The Dr Oz Show was entitled "Anti-Cancer Diet". Dr Oz suggested that three specific foods (endive, red onion and sea bass) are anti-cancer in the sense that they can decrease the risk of ovarian cancer by 75 per cent.

However, Drs Inoue-Choi, Oppeneer and Robien from the Division of Epidemiology and Community Health at the University of Minnesota, authors of the paper "Reality Check: There Is No Such Thing as a Miracle Food", disagreed. They wrote that "the scientific evidence supporting these recommendations is limited". They then went into great detail to explain why they disagreed.

First, the endive. Dr Oz claimed that a chemical called kaempterol would not only stop ovarian cancer cells from growing by destroying their blood supply, but also actively kills ovarian cancer cells. However, this is based on only one prospective observational study, in which endive was one of 39 foods being evaluated. Other foods that were evaluated and had higher levels of kaempterol did not change the risk of ovarian cancer. The protective effect of endives "might have been observed solely by chance."

Second, the red onions. One small study did show a reduced risk of ovarian cancer, but three much larger prospective studies did not. Dr Oz claimed that chemicals called "flavonoids" would reduce ovarian cancer, and specifically recommended red onions. However, red onions do not contain more flavonoids than white or yellow onions.

Third, the sea bass. Once again the researchers found "the evidence of an association between fish intake and ovarian cancer is not convincing".

GREEN TEA

The beverage most conspicuously associated with good health is Green Tea – antioxidants for your health and a soothing aroma for your soul. Indeed, Americans drink 10 billion cups of it each year. The health benefits claimed for Green Tea include lower risks of heart disease and certain cancers.

The various teas (Black, Green, Oolong and White) all come from the same plant – *Camellia sinensis*. The difference between them is the length of time for which the tea leaves are processed and oxidised. Black Tea is oxidised for up to 4 hours, Oolong for about 2 to 3 hours, while Green and White Teas are not oxidised at all. The "wonder ingredients" are antioxidants such as EGCG (epigallocatechin gallate).

According to ConsumerLab.com, an independent US website that tests health products of all kinds, the image of Green Tea does not match up with reality.

If you buy bottled liquid Green Tea, you will often get caffeinated sugar water with hardly any antioxidants. The amounts of antioxidants vary from almost zero up to only 60 per cent of what is advertised on the nutritional label. The bottled drinks can also carry two-thirds as much caffeine as a cup of coffee, as well as up to

18 grams of sugar, half as much as a can of soft drink.

If you buy Green Tea leaves (either loose, or in tea bags) you will get some antioxidants – but some brands had almost as much caffeine as a cup of coffee.

Unfortunately, in 2006 some Green Tea leaves were found to be contaminated with lead. About 85 per cent of Green Tea comes from China. Much of the soil in the Chinese tea-growing areas is contaminated with lead as a result of decades of massive industrial pollution and the use of leaded petrol in cars. The tea plant naturally absorbs more lead from soil than most other plants – especially if the soil is acidic. On the other hand, most of the lead tends to remain in the leaves when they're brewed as tea – in that case, it does not enter your body.

"Eat food. Not too much. Mostly plants." This is very simple, but very deep.

Are the heart and cancer benefits real? Maybe yes and maybe no. In any case, it's best to consume Green Tea in moderation, because very large amounts of it can damage the liver.

But I still enjoy the taste and aroma of the occasional cup of Green Tea.

WHAT TO DO

Michael Pollan, in his book *In Defence Of Food*, makes a very succinct statement: "Eat food. Not too much. Mostly plants." This is very simple, but very deep.

"Food" is something that your parents and grandparents would recognise. It is not highly processed. It is not something that comes vacuum-sealed in a plastic blister pack that needs a chainsaw to open.

"Not too much" refers to the fact that (thanks to 200,000 years of evolution) there is a time delay of about 20 minutes after your stomach is full before your brain recognises that you're full. Back in our distant past, when we found some food, we ate it all immediately – because there might not be any food available tomorrow.

"Plants"? Sure, there are definite health advantages to a well-planned vegetarian diet in adults. But a bit of meat doesn't hurt either, if you have no ethical objections to meat eating.

As Drs Inoue-Choi, Oppeneer and Robien wrote, "Media coverage of . . . so-called miracle foods is often just a marketing tool. Stories of miracle foods sell magazines and advertising space; food industries often sponsor research to show that their foods or products are superior, and supplement industries look to boost sales."

Two and a half thousand years ago, the Greek doctor Hippocrates said, "Let food be thy medicine, and medicine be thy food." It seems as simple as "Eat Food. Not too much. Mostly plants."

Shiny Green

Surprisingly, the colour of the Nutrition Label on food packaging makes a difference. In 2011 in the USA, both the Grocery Manufacturers of America and the Food Marketing Institute introduced a new voluntary labelling system. The label included four basic nutrient categories – calories, saturated fat, sodium and sugar.

Dr Jonathan Schuldt from Cornell University asked 93 students, "Imagine that you are waiting in line in the checkout lane of a grocery store, and that you are hungry. You see a candy bar, and on the front of the candy bar wrapper is a label that shows the calorie content of the candy bar. Please look carefully at the calorie label and the candy bar shown below. Then, answer the questions that follow."

The nutrition label came in three colours – green, red and white. The students thought that the candy bar with a green label was "healthier" than the otherwise identical candy bars that carried red or white labels.

Colours have associations. In many countries, traffic lights use green to mean "go", while red means "stop". Green is also associated with environmentalism, as well as with foods such as spinach and broccoli.

Surprisingly, in this study, those who placed high importance on healthy eating were more likely to view green-labelled foods as being more healthful.

18

GUINEA WORM

The human race has only ever wiped out one single infectious disease – Smallpox. We managed to wipe out Smallpox because it had just one single reservoir – humans, people like you and me. For the same reason, we might be able to eradicate another very nasty infectious disease: Guinea Worm Disease.

Guinea Worm Disease is caused by metre-long worms inside you that release an acid under your skin until your skin ruptures open in blisters. Then the worms slowly and painfully crawl out of the ruptures on your legs, or even your eye sockets. The pain feels like fire and can last for months.

GUINEA WORM HISTORY

The ancient Egyptians described the Guinea Worm 3500 years ago in their medical textbooks. And in the Bible, the Book of Numbers describes how a "plague of fiery serpents" attacked Israelites wandering the deserts – again, Guinea Worms.

And 2000 years ago, both Persian and Greek doctors wrote how to gently wind the worm out of the body by very slowly spinning it on to a stick.

LIFE CYCLE 1 – POND TO HUMAN

The Guinea Worm has a strange life cycle.

The Guinea Worm larva squirms around in the water of a pond that it has just been born into. A Water Flea, hopeful of an easy meal, swallows the larva.

But the Guinea Worm larva is tricky. Once it's inside the gut of the Water Flea, it turns the tables. It does not get digested or broken down. Instead, it just burrows straight out of the gut and into the body cavity of the Water Flea, and eats its testes or ovaries.

This gives the Guinea Worm larva enough food to moult twice over the next few weeks, getting bigger each time. The Water Flea is not just a carrier, it's also a non-consenting nursery for the Guinea Worm.

Despite this rather ferocious start to its life, the Guinea Worm larva will certainly perish – unless a human swallows it. Just like Smallpox, the life cycle of the Guinea Worm can be completed only once inside a human. (Which, by the way, means we can easily break the life cycle of the Guinea Worm – at the water-borne stage – by treating the water.)

When a person drinks infected water from this pond, they'll swallow our Guinea Worm-infected Water Flea. You can't see it with the naked eye because it's so tiny.

The acid juices inside our stomach digest the Water Flea, releasing the Guinea Worm larva, and its life cycle continues.

LIFE CYCLE 2 – GUINEA WORM LOVING

Yes, just like in the Water Flea, the Guinea Worm larva is not bothered by the digestive juices of its host. Again, it repeats its trick of drilling straight out through the wall of the gut. This time it ends up inside the muscles of the person's abdomen. The Guinea Worm larva then starts on a long journey through the human body, usually towards the feet, to find a mate.

After about three or four months, the maturing Guinea Worms roaming through your body are fully grown. The males are only 4 centimetres long. But the females are about a metre long, with most of their body taken up by their gigantic uterus.

The males and females meet somewhere in your muscles and mate. The male then crawls away to die, while the female begins to fatten up to the diameter of a strand of spaghetti, thanks to the three million embryos beginning to grow inside her.

Druggie Guinea Worms

You don't feel the Guinea Worm at any stage of the year-long journey that it takes inside you. In fact, it's totally painless.

This might be because Guinea Worms can make and release the painkiller morphine into their hosts.

Once you've been the Most Powerful
Person in the World, what do you do?

Democratic Ex-President Jimmy Carter went
entirely into "trying to make the world better". Beginning
in 1986, he made it his full-time job to eradicate the Guinea
Worm. In 1989, he used his connections with the DuPont
chemical company to develop a tough yet fine mesh that
could filter the larvae. He also organised donations of "Abate
larvicide from the BASF chemical company, pipes with steel
mesh filters from a Norwegian power company [and]
$16 million from the Bill and Melinda Gates Foundation".

He put his ego far behind himself. He always let the
local "Dictator/President-for-Life/General" in the
local country take all the credit for the eradication of
the Guinea Worm. He was happy to stand in the
background. His unrelenting humility succeeded.

For example, he negotiated a four-month Guinea Worm
Ceasefire in Sudan in 1995. During the Ceasefire, health
workers were able to distribute 200,000 cloth filters to some
2000 villages. They continued to distribute 600,000 cloth
filters each year from 1996 to 2000, and over 800,000 in 2001.
They also distributed over 7.9 million straw filters in 2001 – so
people could drink from potentially contaminated water, even
when away from home. (Wars do tend to displace people
away from their homes, and turn them into refugees.)

LIFE CYCLE 3 – HUMAN TO POND

About nine months later (which is about a year since you drank the infected water), the next generation of Guinea Worm larvae are ready to be born. The mother heads outwards from the muscles for the skin. She pierces through it with chemicals that generate a blister so painful that it feels like intense, relentless burning.

It can take up to three months of unremitting pain before all of the three million larvae have left the mother.

The painful process of waiting for a few months can be slightly sped up by winding the metre-long mother, ever so slowly and gently, onto a stick – and then pulling gently. If you pull too hard, the worm can be torn apart, and the section remaining in the flesh will usually become infected.

For the suffering human, the quickest relief is to rush to the nearest water source and plunge the leg into it.

> Beginning in 1986, former US President Jimmy Carter made it his full-time job to eradicate the Guinea Worm.

The good news about this is that the water slightly, and temporarily, relieves the pain. The bad news is that water stimulates the Guinea Worm mother to vomit out another batch of Guinea Worm larvae from her mouth.

If the water is a pond loaded with some hungry Water Fleas, when the fleas eat the Guinea Worm larvae, the cycle is complete.

HAPPY ENDING

The number of cases of Guinea Worm infection has dropped dramatically, from 50 million in 1947 to around 500 in 2012.

There is no drug or vaccine against the Guinea Worm, nor do people develop immunity to it. Prevention is simple – stop the larvae from getting into your mouth. Methods include: avoiding drinking pond water when the larvae are emerging; getting drinking water from bore holes; spraying insecticides on the pond; boiling drinking water to kill the Water Flea; and using very fine filters inside a drinking straw. All of these will block the Guinea Worm's pathway to your stomach.

> There is no drug or vaccine against the Guinea Worm, nor do people develop immunity to it. Prevention is simple – stop it from getting into your mouth.

Back in 1947, the Guinea Worm infected some 50 million people around the world. The first major blow to the Guinea Worm was the United Nations International Drinking Water Supply and Sanitation Decade (1981–1990). The number of Guinea Worm infections dropped to 3.5 million by 1986, and to 130,000 by 1995.

And thanks to the tireless humanitarian work by former President of the USA Jimmy Carter, in 2012 there were only 542 cases reported in the whole world. The overwhelming majority occurred in South Sudan (521), with the remainder in Chad (10), Mali (7) and Ethiopia (4).

In 2013, President Carter, aged 89, said that he "hopes to outlive the Guinea Worm" – that is, that the Guinea Worm will be extinct before he dies. I hope he does outlive it.

But does that mean that somewhere in the world, some contrarians will start up a "Save the Guinea Worm" movement? Really, the imminent demise of the Guinea Worm is not something worth getting wound up over . . .

19

HIGH-PITCHED HOT CHOCOLATE

It's one of those Simple Things that you notice at the time, but afterwards immediately forget about. It's the clinking sound of a spoon in a cup, and how its pitch seems to change the longer you stir. Of course you know what I'm talking about – the famous Hot Chocolate Effect.

The explanation is that the Sound goes Up, because the Air goes Out.

THE HOT CHOCOLATE EFFECT

You scoop some powdered chocolate into a mug, pour in the steaming hot water, then stir.

Now, if you're a bit obsessive about making sure that all of the chocolate powder gets dissolved, then almost certainly your spoon will clink against the inside of your mug. If you happen to do a lot of clinking, over the next moments you might hear the pitch (or the frequency) of the clinking increase. In fact, it might go up by a whole octave!

It doesn't have to be powdered chocolate – it can occur with any powder that you happen to add hot water to. So it occurs with instant coffee, instant ginseng, and so on.

What's going on?

HISTORY OF THE HOT CHOCOLATE EFFECT

> If you happen to do a lot of clinking, over the next moments you might hear the pitch of the clinking increase. It might go up by a whole octave!

This is not a simple problem to solve. One of the earliest attempts appeared in the prestigious journal *Mathematical Proceedings of the Cambridge Philosophical Society*, which was first published in 1819. In January 1969, when each volume cost a princely 55 shillings, Drs Farrell, McKenzie and Parker offered their humble thoughts on the Hot Chocolate Effect.

Yep, right at the end of a collection of deep scientific papers with fancy, cerebral titles such as "On the Hyper Planes of a Matroid" and "Existence Theorems For H-Space Inverses" appeared their little paper. It had a far more humble and parochial title: "On the Note Emitted from a Mug When Mixing Instant Coffee". They wrote that if "the bottom of the mug was tapped repeatedly with a spoon as the [instant coffee] powder was stirred into the water, the note emitted could be heard to rise in pitch by over an octave."

They thought that this phenomenon could be caused by tiny bubbles of air trapped on the individual grains of the powder, bubbles that were then released into the water. The researchers then wrote about "infinitely long cylindrical shells, flexing modes and eigenfrequency equations". Their calculations did predict a change in pitch of about two octaves, and they went on to write that "we expect similar behaviour from an actual coffee mug" . . . but they didn't carry out any experiments with an actual coffee mug.

> The most striking results are achieved by tapping the bottom of a freshly poured glass of beer.

Maybe coffee was not their favourite drink, as they wrote: "One final piece of experimental work supports our theory. The most striking results are achieved by tapping the bottom of a freshly poured glass of beer. As the cloud of bubbles disperses the ringing tone rises, reaching a constant pitch when the beer is clear."

Why on Earth did they write a theoretical paper on coffee, but experiment on beer? Those crazy physicists . . .

DO THE EXPERIMENT

No, the combination of theory and experiments had to wait until 1982. That was when Dr Frank S. Crawford, a physicist with the famous Laurence Berkeley Laboratory in California, published his work in the *American Journal of Physics*.

Dr Crawford liked to drink lots of hot chocolate. A little unusually, he would get his hot water directly from the hot water tap – not by heating it on a stove or in an electric kettle. Now, the water in your hot water pipes is under high pressure – about four to five times greater than normal atmospheric pressure. And there is air dissolved in this hot, pressurised water. Dr Crawford did lots of deep theorising, made many assumptions, and wrote down over a dozen equations – and then he made predictions, and finally tested them against a series of experiments.

He reckoned that the frequency of sound in water (the rising pitch that he was hearing) was directly related to the speed of sound in water. And he also reckoned that the speed of sound in water was related to just two physical quantities – the density of the water, and the compressibility of the water. The density of water would not change much with temperature – but maybe the compressibility did.

THE SOLUTION

Once the hot water left the high-pressure hot water pipes, all of the dissolved air would try to come out of the solution in the form of tiny bubbles. This "un-dissolving" of the air was helped by the sudden drop in pressure as the hot water left the pressurised water pipe, the presence of the tiny particles of powder (coffee, chocolate, etc.) and the physical act of stirring. As a result, almost immediately, the hot chocolate in the mug was full of microscopic bubbles.

Now normally you can hardly compress water at all. But the presence of this myriad of tiny bubbles made the watery hot chocolate drink much more compressible. The "system" Dr Crawford was considering was the combination of the hot chocolate drink and the clinking spoon. According to his equations, at the very beginning of stirring, the pitch (or the frequency) of the sound generated by the clinking spoon would be low. And over the next minute, again according to his equations, as the bubbles rose to the surface the drink would become less compressible, and the pitch should rise.

When he did the actual experiments, his results agreed with his theories to within 10 per cent.

So it's the opposite of Mary Poppins, where a "spoonful of sugar helps the Medicine go Down". In this case, a spoonful of coffee helps the Sound go Up.

20

HOVERBOARD

Science has given us many wonders and benefits – clean drinking water, vaccines, electricity and space travel. But it has failed us on one very important front.

Australian hip-hop artist Seth Sentry sings on his 2012 debut album, *This Was Tomorrow*, that light bulbs, cyborgs and iPods are "quite cool". Then he asks, "But where's my Hoverboard?"

He has a point. The Hoverboard – basically, a fictional skateboard without wheels that could take you anywhere – is highly desirable. It made its first appearance in 1989 in the movie *Back To The Future II*, so Seth has been waiting a long time. In this movie, our hero Marty McFly made a snappy escape on a Hoverboard. Variations on the Hoverboard have since appeared in other movies and TV shows, video games, animations and books.

On 22 November 2012, "Lee from Cronulla" rang in to the Triple J radio show that Zan Rowe and I host, re-asking the open question that Melbourne rapper Seth Sentry had posed to Science – "But where's my Hoverboard?"

I discussed devices that use "Higgs Boson Technology" to remove mass, and more conventional technology such as Magnetic Levitation.

But Lee said, "I got a skateboard and a blower vac and I taped the blower vac to the skateboard and skated off my roof." He wanted one of our Famous Triple J Fun Packs – basically whatever crap Zan had lying around on her desk (free CDs mostly). He got one. (Luckily, he survived, so he didn't get a Darwin Award.)

The following week, Seth Sentry dropped in while we were on air to say hi.

FOR EVERY ACTION . . .

But how would you actually make a Hoverboard?

You might have heard that "for every action, there is an equal and opposite reaction". This is Newton's Third Law of Motion.

The *Saturn V* multi-stage rocket that took us to the Moon had a Thrust-to-Weight Ratio of around 1.2 at lift-off. Or to rewrite Newton, it Thrust stuff (exhaust gases) downward, so the Weight went upward.

The massive first stage F1 rocket engines generated a Thrust of 3400 tonnes. This Thrust was greater than the Weight of 2800 tonnes, so the engines lifted *Saturn V* off the ground. As *Saturn V* rose, the first stage engines burned through about 1000 tonnes of fuel. As the fuel burned off and the Weight of *Saturn V* decreased, the acceleration increased to 4G. (In other words, the astronauts temporarily weighed four times their regular weight.)

Fuel has Weight

Another factor that helped the acceleration of the *Saturn V* increase after lift-off was the increasingly thinner atmosphere it was rising into.

Not only did the F1 rocket engines become more efficient, but the wind resistance dropped as well. So around 135 seconds after take-off, the Thrust had increased to about 4000 tonnes, while the Weight had dropped to about 1800 tonnes. By that time, the Thrust-to-Weight Ratio had risen to about 2.2.

The excellent Mythbusters team, Jamie Hyneman and Adam Savage, tried to use basic Engineering and leaf blowers to make Hovercraft. Jamie's "Hyneman Hoverboard" and Adam's "Lilypad Flyer" both "worked" – but were rather impractical.

Luckily, Randall Munroe, the creator of xkcd, "a webcomic of romance, sarcasm, math and language", came up with a plan that used Physics to make a Hoverboard. (So far, a prototype for his plan has not been built – thank heavens!)

In his article entitled "Machine Gun Jetpack", he answered the question, "Is it possible to build a jetpack using downward firing machine guns?" That's a definite "Da", if you use Military Engineering.

FIRST, A RUSSIAN MACHINE GUN

Remember Newtown's Third Law of Motion: "For every action there is an opposite and equal reaction"?

If you fire a bullet in one direction, the recoil (or Thrust) will push you in the opposite direction. But that's just one bullet.

Let's ramp up the firepower a bit.

How about a sturdy light machine gun with lots of bullets, specifically the Russian Kalashnikov AK-47? The AK-47 weighs 4.8 kilograms fully loaded with bullets. When you fire the bullets in a continuous stream by holding down your trigger finger, the recoil from the bullets is about 5.9 kilograms. If you factor in the hot gases thrown out and the explosive debris, the recoil increases to about 7.8 kilograms – almost twice the weight of the AK-47. It has a Thrust-to-Weight Ratio of almost 2. So if you stood an AK-47 vertically with the barrel downwards, and pulled the trigger, it would rise into the air – until it ran out of bullets.

> The A-10 is probably the most capable Ground Attack Aircraft ever built, thanks to excellent manoeuvrability, enormous firepower and superb survivability.

A standard AK-47 carries about 30 rounds of ammunition in the magazine. If you made a special magazine that could hold 250 rounds, the AK-47 could just lift its own weight and the 250 rounds off the ground – and the more rounds it fired, the lighter it would get, and the more it would accelerate. If you bolted more than 300 AK-47s together, and stuck them on to the bottom of a large surfboard carrying just a lightweight pilot they could climb over half a kilometre into the sky. The maximum vertical speed would be around 360 kilometres per hour – but hey, watch out below.

SECOND, AN AMERICAN GUN

While the AK-47 "gun" has about twice as much Thrust as Weight, the American GAU-8 Avenger "gun" has about 16 times more Thrust than its Weight.

This is a serious Military–Industrial gun. It fires about 65 bullets each second. Each bullet weighs about 425 grams and is made of aluminium and uranium. This gun is mounted in the American A-10 Ground Attack plane, and while the gun weighs around 281 kilograms, it produces over 4 tonnes of recoil force.

Amazingly, the GAU-8 produces slightly more Thrust (4.5 tonnes) than one of the two engines that power the A-10 (4 tonnes). So if you installed two of these giant GAU-8 Avenger guns in an A-10 and hit the throttle flat out while firing the two guns, the plane would actually slow down. If you had enough bullets, you would end up flying backwards. This gun destroyed armoured tanks on the ground in Iraq, and could easily power a Hoverboard.

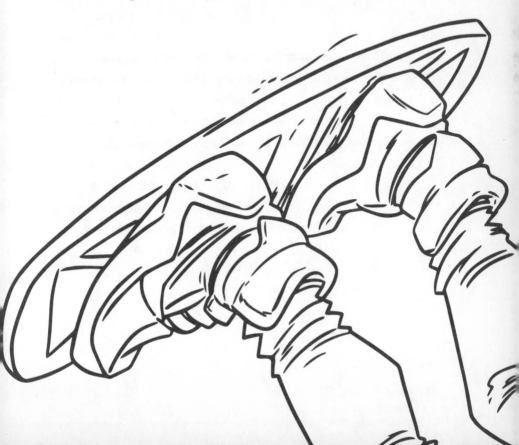

A-10 Thunderbolt

I am a motor-head, and am happy to extend my love of cars to pretty much any engine or machine. I can't help but be very impressed by the A-10.

It's probably the most capable Ground Attack Aircraft ever built, thanks to the ability to loiter around targets for a long time, excellent manoeuvrability, enormous firepower and superb survivability. It can take a huge amount of damage, and still do its "job". It is basically a heavily armoured jet built around a giant seven-barrel Gatling cannon, with the single goal of attacking armoured targets on the ground. The GAU-8 gun is about one-sixth of the weight of the A-10.

On the other hand, attacking anything or anyone doesn't thrill me to bits.

Some 716 A-10s were built between 1972 and 1984, and they will probably keep on flying past 2030. The pilot is protected by a half-tonne titanium "bathtub". The A-10 can fly even when it's missing one engine, one tail, one elevator and half of one wing. But while they are very tough, they are not classically beautiful, and so their nickname is "Warthog".

In the First Gulf War in 1991, they destroyed over 900 Iraqi tanks, 2000 other military vehicles and some 1200 artillery pieces.

THIRD, A RUSSIAN GUN

But the most grunty gun of all would be the Russian GSh-6–30. This terrible gun was mounted in Soviet planes such as the Mikoyan MiG-27, which was used for Ground Attack in the Soviet–Afghanistan War. At 149 kilograms it weighs about half as much as the American GAU-8, and fires at a higher rate (up to 100 rounds per second) giving a Thrust of about 5.5 tonnes. This gives a Thrust-to-Weight Ratio of around 37.

Unfortunately, this awesome thrust had too high a price – and I'm not just talking about the vibration and the noise. The mere act of firing this Russian gun in a MiG-27 could crack the jet's fuel tanks, make the radio and other avionics fail, tear or jam the forward landing doors, force the transparent cockpit canopy to jettison by itself and drop off, and crack the reflector gunsight. More often than not, using the GSh-6–30 would destroy the landing lights. This meant that for night flying, the Mig-27 always had to use runways with floodlights. On one occasion, the "normal" operation of the GSh-6–30 made an instrument panel fall off while the MiG was still flying. And the enormous numbers of fragments created as the bullets smashed into the target would damage any aircraft flying within 200 metres.

Ignoring all the "collateral damage", this Russian GSh-6–30 gun would easily make a Hoverboard barrel along. But only for a while, at a very high price and it would definitely be neither a peaceful ride, nor a controlled situation . . .

21

IS EARTH LOSING WEIGHT?

You see something enormous that we humans have built – say, a huge passenger ship or a gigantic hydroelectric dam – and the question naturally pops into your head: "How much weight did we just add to the planet Earth?" It's a reasonable question.

The answer has two parts. First, by building "stuff" (or increasing the population) we added no new atoms to the Earth. Second, and rather surprisingly, the Earth is getting lighter all the time.

So, first of all, how do you weigh a planet?

Strictly speaking, I should talk about the
"Mass" of the Earth, rather than its "Weight".

Mass is the amount of matter in an object. (Actually,
"Inertial Mass" is a measure of how that object resists
acceleration, but let's keep it simple.) Weight is the force
"felt" by an object, thanks to the local gravitational field.

On Earth, a 1 kilogram body has both a mass and
a weight of 1 kilogram. (Again, more correctly,
weight is a force and so its units are "Newtons",
not "kilograms" – but let's keep it simple.)

On the much smaller and lighter Moon, the weight
of this body is now one-sixth of a kilogram.
Even so, its Mass is still 1 kilogram.

However, "Weight" is what people talk about, so
here I'm using "Weight" instead of "Mass".

HOW TO WEIGH A PLANET

Luckily, Isaac Newton devised the required formula as part of his
Law of Universal Gravitation.

It's theoretically possible to measure the Force of Attraction
between two bodies or weights (such as two lead balls in a lab) and
plug that result into Newton's formula to work out the Gravitational
Constant. Then you reuse his formula to work out the weight of
our planet. Newton never thought it would be possible, with an
experiment carried out on Earth, to actually measure this Attractive

Force between two bodies. He thought the tiny attraction between the two lead balls in the experiment would be swamped by the absolutely gigantic attraction caused by the huge mass of our planet.

However, Isaac Newton didn't account for the cleverness of the Reverend John Mitchell. Mitchell lived in the 18th century and was not only the "Father of Seismology" but also the first person to make a reasonable estimate of the distance to a star other than our Sun (Vega). He was also the first person to float the possibility of Black Holes. In the early 1780s, he built an experiment to measure the Force of Attraction between two lead balls. He died before he could use this apparatus, which, upon his death, passed to the scientist Henry Cavendish.

In 1798, Cavendish rebuilt the apparatus with some minor improvements, and successfully measured the Force of Attraction between two lead balls that weighed 0.73 kilograms and 158 kilograms. He then plugged his results into Newton's formula and came up with a very good estimate for the weight of the Earth. Cavendish was within about 1 per cent of what we now know is the true result – about 6 billion trillion tonnes.

HEAVIER OR LIGHTER?

So, when you build something really big, does the Earth get heavier?

No. All you're doing is shifting atoms from one location on the Earth to another location.

When you build a giant ship, you just shift iron ore from Western Australia to blast furnaces in China and on to shipyards in Korea. Overall, nothing gets added to or taken away from our planet, because the Earth functions almost as a perfectly closed system.

(However, moving stuff around on the surface of the Earth can change its rotation.)

INPUTS AND OUTPUTS

But our Earth is not quite a 100 per cent closed system. There are Inputs, and there are Outputs. That is, there's stuff falling out of the sky down onto the Earth, and there's junk going up into space, such as all those spacecraft we launch.

So let's do the major numbers for these Inputs and Outputs.

The Earth gains about 40,000 tonnes of dust each year. The vast majority of this dust is stuff left over from when our solar system was formed. The gravitational field of our Earth just sucks it in as our planet orbits the Sun. A decent meteor storm can add a tonne in a single go.

What about losses?

Each year about 95,000 tonnes of hydrogen and 1600 tonnes of helium leave the Earth for outer space. They're gone forever. These gases are very low in mass, and the average molecules move very quickly indeed. So the faster molecules can achieve the so-called "Escape Velocity" and leave the Earth forever.

As another loss, what about the rockets that we send into space? After all, the gigantic *Saturn V* rocket that took us to the Moon weighed just under 3000 tonnes on the launch pad. But the overwhelming majority of those rockets and their fuel have fallen back to earth. If you do the numbers, it works out that each year only about 65 tonnes of rocket payload – very expensive payload – leaves the Earth for ever.

So, basically, each year the Earth gains about 40,000 tonnes, and loses about 95,000 tonnes. Overall, our planet gets lighter by about 55,000 tonnes each year.

That works out to about 890,000 people (average weight 62 kilograms), or about half the weight of one of those giant passenger liners, or about 0.000 000 000 000 001 per cent of the mass of our planet.

But that's not enough to translate into a lucrative bestseller on the massive weight-loss industry charts.

Energy is Mass is Energy . . .

Most of us have heard of Einstein's famous "$E = mc^2$" equation, where "E" is "energy", "m" is "mass" and "c" is the "speed of light".

This equation says that energy and mass are different forms of the same stuff. You can think of mass as coagulated (or frozen) energy, while energy is just mass that's been unleashed or set loose. (This is not strictly correct, but it's close enough.)

Surprisingly, a hot cup of coffee is heavier than a cold cup. (It's a very tiny effect – if a kilogram heats up by 1°C, it will gain 1.5 trillionths of a gram.) Thanks to Global Warming, the surface of the Earth is trapping an extra 0.6 watts per square metre from the Sun. That works out to 20 times the power usage of the entire human race, or the same as exploding 400,000 Hiroshima atomic bombs every day. And it works out to 160 tonnes of added weight each year.

The core of our planet generates its heat from the radioactive decay of uranium, potassium and thorium. But the core is slowly cooling down. This works out to a mass loss of 16 tonnes each year.

Overall, these weights (160 tonnes and 16 tonnes) make very minor changes to the enormously larger weight of our planet.

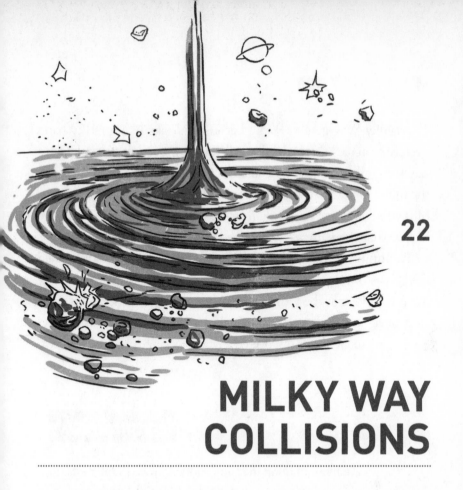

22

MILKY WAY COLLISIONS

Whenever we city dwellers get far enough out of the Big Smoke that we leave the city lights behind, at some stage we'll look up and marvel at the Milky Way blazing across the night sky. Our Sun (with its little family of planets) is just one of the 400 billion or so stars in the Milky Way. The Milky Way is our home galaxy. Our Solar System is out in the suburbs of our galaxy, about 26,000 light years from the centre, roughly halfway to the edge.

The Milky Way looks so beautifully quiet and peaceful – but it's not. Right now, our Milky Way galaxy is cannibalising a smallish Dwarf Galaxy. In a while it will collide with a galaxy called Andromeda – and did I mention that the monstrous Black Hole in the centre of the Milky Way is warming up for its first decent meal in quite some time?

MILKY WAY 101

The Milky Way gets its name because it looks like a milky band stretching across the night sky. All you can see with the naked eye is a fuzzy milky glow. You need binoculars or a telescope to pick out the individual stars. It was only in the 1920s that we realised that the Milky Way was just one of many galaxies in our Universe. Today we reckon that there are a few hundred billion galaxies.

Beginning in the 1970s and 1980s, our astronomers developed new types of telescopes – both on the ground and in space. They didn't only look at the visible Milky Way – they also checked out the electromagnetic radiation it was emitting between microwaves and X-rays, and suddenly we discovered a whole lot more about our galaxy.

Violent Galaxy

We used to think that our Milky Way was just a boring average galaxy, with nothing new or exciting happening, settling into a comfortable and humdrum middle age. But, in the words of Ann Finkbeiner, writing in the journal *Nature*, the Milky Way "was born in chaos and shaped by violence . . . it lives in a state of turbulent complexity, and . . . its future holds certain catastrophe".

Scattered around our Milky Way are Stellar Nurseries, where gas is being made into stars at the rate of a few times the mass of our Sun every year. The stars range from huge to average to small. These tumultuous areas eject enormous amounts of ultraviolet radiation as well as huge amounts of regular matter in the form of stellar winds. Some of the newborn stars have enormous mass and die quickly in supernova explosions, while the stars that are not quite as massive expand into Red Giants, roughly the size of the orbit of the Earth around the Sun. I think of these massive stars as the Janis Joplins of stars – they live fast, die young.

There seem to be thin halos of stars extending way past the traditional boundaries of the Milky Way, reaching out some 300,000 light years from the central Black Hole.

Wrong Name

Why is the Black Hole at the centre of our Milky Way galaxy called Sagittarius A*? The centre is very important, and it's in the constellation Sagittarius, so it's called both "A" and "*" to show how important it is. It's pronounced "Sagittarius A star", and usually shortened in writing to Sgr A*.

But why the asterisk? It turns out the Astronomers had made an entirely reasonable mistake. There's a lot happening at the centre of our Milky Way – Black Holes, lots of stars, gas clouds and so on. It's hard to pin down the exact centre. After a lot of hard work, the Astronomers were pretty sure that some gas clouds were the centre. So they named those clouds "Sagittarius A".

Later they realised their mistake. The name "Sagittarius A" was already used up, so they called the Black Hole "Sagittarius A*".

MILKY WAY CANNIBAL

First, the cannibalism.

Twice in the past two billion years, a Dwarf Galaxy called Sagittarius has blasted through our Milky Way galaxy (which is about 10,000 times larger). No stars have actually collided, but many thousands of stars have been torn out of Sagittarius to form huge loops that rise out of our galaxy and then swoop back in again. These loops, known as the Sagittarius Stream, will become part of our galaxy. So our Milky Way is getting bigger by shredding and "eating" this Dwarf Galaxy.

In fact, there seem to be remnants of possibly hundreds of Dwarf Galaxies in the space just outside our Milky Way. What we see are many separate faint lines of stars that rise out into space away from our Milky Way, and then loop back down into the body of our galaxy.

Maybe there's been a lot of cannibalism going on.

Past Black Hole Activity

Something big and interesting (we're not exactly sure what) happened to our Black Hole about 10 million years ago. As a result, it squirted out huge jets of energy and created huge shockwaves.

The net result was two symmetrical back-to-back bubbles of hot gas shooting out on each side of our Milky Way – one above and one below. They are very energetic – outlined by X-rays, with accompanying gamma-ray jets. And they are enormous – reaching out about 25,000 light years away from the Black Hole.

MILKY WAY COLLIDES WITH ANDROMEDA

Second, in about five billion years or so, our Milky Way galaxy will collide with something its own size, or a bit bigger. Yup, say hello to the Andromeda galaxy, currently about 2.5 million light years away, but approaching on a collision course at around 400,000 kilometres per hour.

> At around the end of 2013 the enormous Black Hole in the centre of our galaxy will have its first real meal in quite some time.

Again, it's almost certain that no stars will actually collide, because space is so big and stars are so small in comparison.

But the Milky Way will change its shape in a rather drastic makeover, and our Sun will most likely be tossed into a different region in our galaxy, probably further from the centre. After a few billion years and a few frantic orbits around each other, the two spiral galaxies (Milky Way and Andromeda) will merge, and the trillion or so stars will probably settle into an elliptical-shaped galaxy. I wish I were like Dr Who and could go to the future in the TARDIS to see this.

OUR BLACK HOLE STARTS FEEDING

And third, at around the end of 2013 the enormous Black Hole in the centre of our galaxy will have its first real meal in quite a while. This Black Hole, Sagittarius A*, is about four million times the mass of our Sun.

To get that big, Sgr A* must have eaten lots of stars and other stuff, but it's been sleeping and on a near-starvation diet for centuries. A Black Hole can eat lots, which is why it gets to be so big, but it's not a fast eater.

But now it's time for tucker . . .

Over the past few years, astronomers have been tracking a huge gas cloud heading for the Black Hole in the centre of our galaxy. It's not on a head-on collision course but will skim past. Even so, some of the gas cloud will end up inside Sgr A*.

This should all be very exciting for the people who prophesied our imminent doom in 2012 according to the Mayan Calendar.

This cloud, called (rather unromantically) G2, will make its closest approach to Sgr A* late in 2013, or early in 2014. It will approach awfully close to our Black Hole – only 30 billion kilometres away, or about seven times the distance from the Sun to Neptune. G2 is probably just a big cloud of gas and dust, or it might be a cloud of gas and dust wrapped around a small star. In fact, we don't even know where it came from. At the time of writing it's zipping in towards the Black Hole at 2400 kilometres per second, but will speed up as it gets closer.

As the gas cloud gets closer, the massive gravity of Sgr A* will start shredding G2's gas and dust into long spaghetti-like filaments or strands. There might be some decent X-rays flaring off from the gas. A month or two later, most of the shredded gas filaments should collide with the so-called "Accretion Disc". This is a swirling flattened doughnut of stuff that both surrounds and feeds the Black Hole. This collision could generate all kinds of radiation – from X-rays to radio waves (and maybe some gamma rays as well).

First, remnants of G2 collide with the Accretion Disc. Then, over the next few months (or years or even decades), these remnants spiral through the Disc and continue on, to plummet into the Black Hole's Event Horizon – and vanish inside forever. This final plunge could again create violent electromagnetic fireworks.

(Of course, *if* there's a star hidden inside the gas cloud and *if* the star hits the Accretion Disc and *if* it enters the Black Hole, *then* the fireworks will be spectacular.)

This should all be very exciting for the people who prophesied our imminent doom in 2012 according to the Mayan Calendar, and from the Large Hadron Collider a few years earlier. They will be out in force for this cosmic collision.

And in terms of keeping some perspective, if things haven't been going so well for you personally, you can comfort yourself with this thought: at least you're not getting sucked into a Black Hole's Event Horizon, and then disappearing forever from the Universe.

Flaring Black Hole

The astronomer Fred Hoyle, who both disagreed with the Big Bang Theory of the Universe and gave the Theory its name, published a book, *The Inferno*, in 1973.

It deals with what happens when the Black Hole in the centre of our Milky Way galaxy flares up. It flares up so much that dangerous amounts of radiation bathe our planet. The Milky Way is not very visible from the far northern latitudes – so the main characters in the book move to the safety of Scotland.

Black Hole

The size of a star is given by the balance of two forces –
the nuclear fires pushing out, and gravity sucking in.

If the star (after the nuclear fires go out) is less than
1.4 times the mass of our Sun, it will eventually collapse down
to a White Dwarf (one to two times the size of the Earth).
If it's between 1.4 and 3 times the mass of our Sun, it will
collapse to a Neutron Star (8 to 20 kilometres across).
A Black Hole is usually formed when a big star (more than
10 times the mass of our Sun) collapses, after the nuclear
fires burn out. It will collapse down to Zero Volume – not just
small, or really small, but Zero – a point called a Singularity.
That's physicist talk for "the Laws of Physics are broken".

Inside a Black Hole, time and space as we understand
them no longer exist. Its gravity is so strong that nothing,
not even light, can escape. In fact, the Event Horizon that
surrounds the Black Hole is defined as the point of no return
– it's a boundary in Space–Time through which matter
and light can only pass one way, inwards.

While the Black Hole has no size, the Event Horizon does.
If the Black Hole is about 10 times the mass of our Sun,
the Event Horizon is about 60 kilometres across. For a Black
Hole 1000 times our Sun's mass, it's about 60,000 kilometres.
For Sgr A*, it's about 26 million kilometres – by comparison,
Earth's orbit is about 280 million kilometres across.

23

MONEY MAGNETS: THE SCIENCE OF ECONOMICS

"We are the 99 per cent" is the slogan of the Occupy movement. Their complaint is that while 1 per cent of the US population controls 40 per cent of the wealth, the remaining 99 per cent of US citizens have to share 60 per cent of the wealth.

Why do the rich have all the money? How did so few people get so wealthy? Why is it almost a Law of Nature that most of a society's wealth falls into the hands of a minority? Can money make you happy? Can poverty make you sick? And can physics help economics do a better job?

The Occupy Movement

Occupy is an international protest movement with the goal of redressing massive economic (and corresponding social and health) inequalities.

It began in mid-May 2011 as the Spanish *Indignado* movement. It spread rapidly and achieved worldwide publicity with Occupy Wall Street on 17 September 2011. By 9 October, Occupy protests had occurred in some 82 countries, in every continent except for Antarctica.

The main concern of the Occupy movement is its belief that the global financial system works hand in hand with large corporations to give massive, unfair benefits to a tiny minority. The Occupy movement claims that this action undermines democracy – and, as a result, can lead to a society that is unstable.

To counteract this, the Occupy movement has clear goals, which have changed a little over time. Its members originally wanted to "tighten banking industry regulations, ban high-frequency trading, arrest all 'financial fraudsters' responsible for the 2008 crash, and form a Presidential Commission to investigate and prosecute corruption in politics".

Hidden $

In 1663, diarist Samuel Pepys wrote, "At dinner they did discourse very finely to us of the probability that there is a *vast deal of money* hid in the land."

"THAT'S NOT FAIR"

One of the first signs that children are developing a Sense of Morality is when they cry, "But that's not fair!"

Members of the Occupy movement were disturbed by what they saw as unfair – a recent worldwide trend for more and more wealth to concentrate in the hands of a smaller and smaller percentage of our society.

Let me give three examples.

First, in July 2012, the global Tax Justice Network released a report, *The Price of Offshore Revisited*. It was researched by James S. Henry, the former Chief Economist for management consulting firm McKinsey and Co. He claimed that a relatively small number of High Net Worth Individuals from some 139 countries had secreted away huge amounts of cash from their respective countries' Tax Offices. This cash (not assets such as houses, cars, yachts or private jets) had been transferred via banks such as UBS, Credit Suisse and Goldman Sachs to various offshore tax havens.

Henry claimed about 92,000 people (about 0.0013 per cent of the world's population) held about US$9.8 trillion in concealed offshore accounts.

According to the report, fewer than 10 million people (about 0.0014 per cent of the world's population, and that includes the 92,000 people above) had hidden away from their local Tax Offices some US$21–32 trillion. That sum is roughly equal to the size of the US and Japanese economies combined.

If that US$21–32 trillion earned about 3 per cent interest, and if that interest was taxed at a conservative 30 per cent, it would generate annual tax revenue of US$190 to $280 billion.

Second, let's look at a 2011 report from the US Congressional Budget Office. It looked at the after-tax household income of US citizens between 1979 and 2007, adjusted for inflation. For the top 1 per cent of the US population, this income grew by 275 per cent. For the top 20 per cent (including the top 1 per cent), it grew by 65 per cent. For the top 67 per cent, it grew by 40 per cent. And for the bottom 20 per cent, after-tax household income grew by just 18 per cent over that 18-year period.

Third, consider the whole Planet. The poorer 50 per cent of the world's population hold just 1 per cent of the total wealth.

These examples are just the tip of the iceberg regarding the ever-widening gap between the wealthy and the poor.

ECONOMICS 101

According to the *Encyclopaedia Britannica*, economics is the "social science that seeks to analyse and describe the production, distribution and consumption of wealth". It looks at how you make wealth, spread it around and use it up.

The history of economics goes back a long way.

The earliest case of economic warfare that we know of happened in Ancient Greece, prior to the Peloponnesian War of 431–404 BC. Here the belligerents blockaded each other and intercepted each other's supplies. In general, economic warfare is where one country tries to weaken another country either by stopping it from getting financial, technological or physical resources, or by stopping it from trading with other countries. Typical tools of economic warfare include boycotts, tariff discrimination, freezing of capital, trade embargoes, prohibition of aid and the simple taking of any financial resources you can get your hands on.

As a recent example, in the 1990s the USA finally defeated the Soviet Union (and Soviet Communism) after half a century of economic warfare that on the US side included embargoes on computers and other high-technology equipment. But, more importantly, the Soviets went bankrupt in a futile attempt to match massive American military spending. (Current annual US military spending is greater than the next top nine countries' military spending put together.)

The Ancient Greeks thought deeply about economics. Then there was a long gap in Western economic theories until the 15th to 18th centuries AD, when Renaissance scholars began to produce an enormous body of literature in the form of pamphlets. They came up with an economic theory called "Mercantilism", which was basically about protectionism. (Protectionism is about protecting your own countries' interests by fees, tariffs, quotas, etc. It's the opposite of "Free Trade", in which government barriers are kept to a minimum.)

The earliest case of economic warfare that we know of happened in Ancient Greece, prior to the Peloponnesian War of 431–404 BC.

Modern economics probably began in the year 1776, when the Scottish thinker Adam Smith published his great work *An Inquiry into the Nature and Causes of the Wealth of Nations*. He looked at the economic development of nations, and what forces could encourage or hinder this growth. He also looked at the "Free-Enterprise System", how it could affect what people did, and how people's activities could in turn affect the free-enterprise system.

For example, as a single individual I have a very small influence on the local economy. As an individual, all I can do is either buy or not buy goods, or sell or not sell. I can also decide how many of these goods I shall buy or sell.

THE PHYSICS OF ECONOMICS, PART 1 – MAXWELL-BOLTZMANN DISTRIBUTION

But here's the weird part. One single individual can't usually do much in a free-enterprise system – and yet the sum of all the actions of individuals like me determines what the final price will be.

This "behaviour" sounds suspiciously like what happens in many branches of Physics.

For example, in a gas an individual molecule will travel at a certain speed, which determines its temperature. In turn, the average speed of all the molecules determines the overall temperature of the gas. Taking this a little further, the Maxwell-Boltzmann Distribution describes how much energy is carried by different molecules in a gas.

This broad curve looks remarkably like the curve that describes how much money is earned by different people in a society. When molecules meet in a collision, they keep some of their energy and exchange the remainder. In the same way, when people meet in a commercial transaction, they keep some of their wealth and exchange the rest.

> The econophysicists made the analogy that individual people, and their economic power, are like atoms in poorly condensed matter.

Most of the gas molecules will travel at around the average speed. But a small number will (as a result of their various collisions) travel somewhat faster. In the same way, a small number of people will be somewhat wealthier.

This tantalising link is why, for over a century, some physicists have forayed into the strange land of economics. They're called "econophysicists". (I should mention that their overall School of Thought is not inside the mainstream of Economics.) They've shown that it seems almost to be a Law of Nature that most of the wealth will fall into the hands of a minority.

THE PHYSICS OF ECONOMICS, PART 2 – THE ULTRA-WEALTHY

In our society, it is claimed (often bitterly) that there is "one law for the rich, and another for everyone else". Some econophysicists agree. The Maxwell-Boltzmann Distribution covers most people – but another Law covers the ultra-wealthy.

These econophysicists come from the field of Condensed Matter, which deals with the atoms and molecules that make up the world around us. Sometimes, when atoms condense from a gas into a solid or liquid, they do so into relatively well-ordered patterns (for example, crystals or metal). But sometimes the matter condenses poorly. In this case, the atoms don't fall into neat patterns, but instead condense into many small, disordered arrangements (for example, glass or some plastics).

The econophysicists made the analogy that individual people, and their economic power, are like atoms in poorly condensed matter. They stirred all this economics and physics knowledge together, and added a simple assumption: that life is unpredictable. They also added in the effect of temperature – and bingo, they found the Pareto Law of Wealth Distribution appearing in their equations.

VILFREDO PARETO, MR 80:20

Vilfredo Pareto lived from 1848 to 1923. He started his career as an engineer, but then became a philosopher, sociologist, political scientist and economist.

Benoit Mandelbrot, the Polish-born mathematician who founded the field of Fractal Mathematics, wrote of Pareto, "His legacy as an economist was profound. Partly because of him, the field evolved from a branch of moral philosophy as practiced by Adam Smith into a data intensive field of scientific research and mathematical equations."

Pareto worked out that in Italy, 20 per cent of the population owned 80 per cent of the property. He found similar ratios when he analysed other financial data over time in different countries. He studied the tax records from 1454 for Basel in Switzerland from 1741, 1498 and 1512 for Augsburg in Germany, 20th century rental incomes in Paris, and personal incomes from Italy, Iceland, Peru, Saxony, Prussia and the UK. He found similar patterns everywhere he looked – sometimes it was 80:20, or perhaps 70 per cent of the income was collected by just 30 per cent of the population. There was not a steady drop in the number of people as the wealth increased. Instead it was like a champagne coupe turned upside-down – very wide at the bottom with lots of poor people, and very thin at the top with very few wealthy people.

He is now famous for Pareto's Law. It states that the number of people who have Wealth (W) is proportional to $1/W^E$. Back then in 1897, "E" was always between "2" and "3", regardless of whether the society was peasant agricultural Russia, or sophisticated industrial England. Although the world has changed enormously since 1897, "E" is still between "2" and "3" – and even today, a tiny minority of the people control most of the wealth.

Today, with the extreme widening of the gap between the super-wealthy and the rest of us, we need another set of mathematics to fully describe the situation. The Maxwell-Boltzmann Distribution describes most of us, while one part of the Pareto Law (the Pareto Tail) deals with the ultra-wealthy.

80:20 Rule

The Pareto Law is seen in the sizes of sand particles and meteorites, and in the values of oil reserves in oilfields (there are many small oilfields, and only a few large ones). It applies in the insurance business, which deals with many small claims, and only a few big ones. It's important in the field of Hydrology, relating to maximum one-day rainfalls and river discharges – again, lots of small ones and only a few big ones.

In business it appears as the truism "80 per cent of your sales come from 20 per cent of your clients".

In 2002, Paula Rooney of Microsoft said that 80 per cent of their computer crashes and errors were caused by the top 20 per cent most reported bugs in their software.

It is also claimed that 20 per cent of US patients are responsible for 80 per cent of health care costs, and that 20 per cent of criminals commit 80 per cent of all crimes.

The first thing to note is that this 80:20 rule is just an approximation and definitely not an exact rule. The second thing to note is that the two numbers don't have to add up to 100, because they're measuring different things. For example "sales" and "clients" are different and cannot be added. But it is "neat" if they do add up to 100.

HAPPINESS AND MONEY

The writer H.L. Mencken quipped, "a wealthy man is one who earns $100 a year more than his wife's sister's husband." The happiness that money can bring us depends on how much money the people around us have.

Dr Michael I. Norton carried out a study on wages in the USA. He found the people who most vehemently did not want any increase in the minimum wage were the people who earned just a bit more than the minimum wage. If there was an increase in the minimum wage, these people would no longer be in the second poorest group in the USA, but the poorest group.

In the study, the money-makes-you-happier effect tapered off around a yearly salary of US$75,000. This is well below the US$350,000 per annum needed to scrape into the richest 1 per cent of US citizens. The situation is *not* that more money makes you unhappy – instead, a lot more cash simply doesn't make you a lot happier. (In fact, there is a theory for these "Diminishing Marginal Returns".)

Indeed, many of us have fond memories of being deliriously happy at times in our life when we were desperately poor.

But other research by Dr Norton shows that one surprising way to gain happiness with money is to give it away. You can turn money into happiness by giving it to family, friends or a charity – or even buying coffee for a colleague.

HEALTH AND MONEY

The evidence is overwhelming that poverty brings with it poor health – as well as crime and other social ills. This litany of woes includes alcoholism, heart disease, suicide attempts, chronic obstructive pulmonary disease, premature death and so on.

This is related to many factors, including a higher risk of exposure to violence, plus less access to healthcare, education and nutritious food. For another factor, children in the UK whose parents have never worked or who are long-term unemployed are 13 times more likely to die from an injury or poisoning accident than children of wealthy parents. These factors are thought to be exacerbated by the Poverty Trap – a self-reinforcing mechanism that appears to cause poverty to persist from generation to generation.

Another factor is the persistent stress of trying to survive as a poor person in a hostile world. In the short term, the "Stress Response" is a powerful and appropriate survival mechanism. It sends extra glucose through the bloodstream, and increases your breathing rate, heart rate and blood pressure. All of this combines so that your muscles can work really well in an emergency. And to protect you from losing too much blood in case you're wounded, the clotting chemicals in your blood increase and the blood vessels shrink.

> You can turn money into happiness by giving it to family, friends or a charity – or even buying coffee for a colleague.

But in the long term, the "Stress Response" can make you unwell. You suffer an increased risk of diabetes, high blood pressure and blood clots – and your immune system can weaken.

And this leads to earlier deaths.

One measure of economic disparity is the Gini Coefficient, which ranges from 0 to 1. At 0 everybody earns the same, while at 1 one person takes all the money. Most countries range between 0.63 (South Africa) and 0.25 (Denmark). Once the Gini Coefficient gets higher than 0.3, that country begins to experience unnecessary and avoidable deaths from poverty-related health problems.

According to a 2004 study by S.V. Subramanian and colleagues from the Harvard School of Public Health, the USA, with a Gini Coefficient of 0.36, had nearly 900,000 avoidable deaths. The UK, with a score of 0.33, had about 12,000 avoidable deaths. Current British financial inequalities, and the accompanying avoidable deaths, are greater than those seen during the economic depression of the 1930s.

THE FIXES

One of the discoveries of the econophysicists is that no matter what we do, a small percentage of people will always control most of the wealth. But that does not have to be a bad thing.

First, worldwide poverty seems to be dropping. The term "absolute poverty" is specifically defined as having to survive on less than US$1.25 per day. According to 2008 World Bank statistics, the situation has improved since 1981. Back then 1.94 billion people lived in absolute poverty, as compared to 1.29 billion more recently. On the other hand, nobody should have to survive in absolute poverty and live on less than US$1.25 per day. Fixing this should be a priority.

> Justice Oliver Wendell Holmes of the US Supreme Court said that "taxes are what we pay for civilized society".

Second, it seems inevitable that in any modern society, most of the money will gravitate to a minority of the people. It has a lot to do with luck and, of course, it helps a lot if your parents are wealthy. Even if a revolution happens and the rich and powerful people are killed, soon a new and different bunch of rich and powerful people will arise.

And from a practical point of view, if we all get a decent bite of the cherry, it doesn't matter as much if a minority is fabulously wealthy. So long as my family and I have access to high-quality medical care and education, and a just legal system, we don't need access to three cars (we have one car and four bikes).

Third, the temperature of the economy is important. If the economy is hot and vigorous with lots of trading, then money will spread around, creating lots of new wealthy people. But if the economy is cold, and there's not much trading, the wealth freezes and stays where it is. It can't flow to other people. This can be the case in some unsettled or developing nations. For example, in Mexico the wealthiest 40 people control 30 per cent of all the money.

Fourth, fair taxes help spread the money around. If you increase the taxes a little, so that "E" in Pareto's Law equals "3", you shift the money around so that the wealthiest 20 per cent of the population control not 80 per cent of the money but only 55 per cent. It's not totally fair, but it is much better. Unfortunately, in the real world the wealthy can organise their affairs with expensive lawyers and accountants so that they might end up paying very little tax anyway.

However, Justice Oliver Wendell Holmes of the US Supreme Court said that he preferred to pay his taxes over any other of his bills, because "taxes are what we pay for civilized society".

From time to time, governments will "adjust" the taxes – and surprisingly often, in such a way as to widen the gap between the wealthy and the poor. In the Australian 2005 Budget, the Treasurer Peter Costello gave bigger tax cuts to the wealthiest 5 per cent of households (who didn't *need* them) than to the poorest 50 per cent (who definitely *did* need them). The same situation arose in the US as a result of George W. Bush's tax "adjustments". As Edmund L. Andrews of *The New York Times* wrote in 2007, "Rich families were the undisputed winners from President Bush's tax cuts . . ."

Fifth, save money. The wealthiest 10 per cent of the population are much more likely to save their money. Obviously it's easier to save if you have more disposable income. On the other hand, the economists and the econophysicists tell us that when more people save, the financial inequalities of a society begin to level out.

HEALTHY, WEALTHY AND WISE?

If these econophysicists are really onto something new, maybe they can help turn economics into a science.

This might mean that a new "scientifically balanced economics" could give us a society in which we have full employment with reasonable working hours, social justice, and fair health, education and welfare entitlements – and no repeating boom-and-bust cycles in which some people's lives are torn apart and thrown on the scrap heap. And then money could really make the world go round . . .

No Economics Nobel Prize?

People say that Economics must be a "Science" because there is a Nobel Prize for it. Neither part of this statement is true.

It's not a "Science". Science is a process that tries to understand the Universe around us (according to Wikipedia and the Encyclopaedia). To do this, Science uses unbiased observations and systematic experimentation to build knowledge in the form of testable explanations and predictions. Economics is pretty good at observing what has happened. But it's not as good at making accurate predictions – for example, what will happen if you increase the subsidy on butter, or decrease real taxes.

There is also no Nobel Prize for Economics. Alfred Nobel (the inventor of dynamite) was very wealthy. His will stipulated that part of his fortune should be "annually distributed in the form of prizes to those who, during the preceding year, shall have conferred the greatest benefit to mankind". On 10 December 1901 (five years after Nobel died) the first Nobel Prizes were awarded in Peace, Physics, Chemistry, Physiology or Medicine, and Literature.

Much later, in 1969, the first "Bank of Sweden Prize in Economic Sciences in Memory of Alfred Nobel" was awarded. It is funded by the Bank of Sweden, not from Nobel's estate. However, it is awarded at the same ceremony as the "real" Nobel Prizes – hence the "confusion".

24

OCEAN ACIDIFICATION

Back in 1988, after Dr James Hansen had testified to US Congressional Committees and given them the hard data, we knew that Global Warming was real. (Global Warming used to be called the "Greenhouse Effect". Nowadays it's called "Climate Change".) That was a quarter of a century ago.

Since then, Climate Change has continued at an increasing rate. In the Arctic, since 1980 the warming climate has melted about 80 per cent of the volume of late summer ice. (That's correct: not 8 per cent or 18 per cent, but 80 per cent!) In addition, the permafrost that covers a quarter of the land area in the Northern Hemisphere has begun to release greenhouse gases – again, due to Climate Change.

OCEANS TURN MORE ACID

But besides the Heating, there's another aspect of Climate Change – its evil offsider, Ocean Acidification. That's right, we humans are making the oceans more acid.

About one quarter of the carbon dioxide we have dumped into the atmosphere has been soaked up by the oceans. As the carbon dioxide dissolves into the seawater, it makes it slightly more acid.

I don't mean that the ocean will burn your skin next time you go for a swim. No, the oceans have shifted from being slightly alkaline to just a little bit less alkaline.

When you measure acidity and alkalinity in numbers you use the pH scale, which ranges from 0 to 14. Something really acid, like stomach acid, has a pH of 1, while something very alkaline, like bleach, has a pH of 13. Distilled water is neutral – neither acid nor alkaline – and has a pH of 7.

pH Chemistry

The pH scale tells you how acid (or non-acid, or alkaline) something is. If a liquid is very acidic, it has a very low pH number. It has more protons (or hydrogen ions, H^+) than something that is less acidic.

Surprisingly, the exact meaning of "pH" is disputed, even though it was first introduced in 1909 by the Danish chemist Søren Peder Lauritz Sørensen. Many chemists have settled on "pH" as meaning "power of hydrogen".

One hundred and fifty years ago, the oceans used to have an average pH of 8.2, but they now have a pH of 8.1, a tiny bit closer towards the acid end of the pH scale. "Wait," I hear you cry, "surely a slight drift of 0.1 towards the acid end of the scale would have no effect on the oceans?"

A downward shift of 0.1 in the oceanic pH actually means a colossal 30 per cent increase in the number of protons (H^+). This is because the pH scale is not linear, it's logarithmic.

So, it does effect the oceans. Many sea creatures need carbonate ions to make calcium carbonate ($CaCO_3$), which is the basis for their calcium-based infrastructure (skeleton, shell, etc).

$$Ca^{2+} + CO_3^{2-} \leftrightarrow CaCO_3$$

(The double-ended arrow means that the reactions can go in either direction, depending on the external conditions).

A little carbon dioxide is good – and essential for these sea creatures.

Too much carbon dioxide is bad.

Adding excess carbon dioxide to seawater dramatically reduces the amount of carbonate that is available for sea creatures. As a result, they can no longer make calcium carbonate for their skeletons and shells. These creatures include coral, plankton, coralline algae, mussels, sea urchins, krill and pteropods.

With today's ocean pH of 8.1, about 90 per cent of the total dissolved inorganic carbon is bicarbonate (HCO_3^-), 9 per cent is carbonate (CO_3^{2-}), and only 1 per cent is dissolved carbon dioxide (CO_2) and carbonic acid (H_2CO_3).

When carbon dioxide (CO_2) dissolves in water (H_2O), it can form carbonic acid (H_2CO_3), which then can break up into a proton (H^+) and a bicarbonate ion (HCO_3^-), or two protons ($2H^+$) and a carbonate ion (CO_3^{2-}).

$$CO_2 + H_2O \leftrightarrow H_2CO_3 \leftrightarrow H^+ + HCO_3^- \leftrightarrow 2H^+ + CO_3^{2-}$$

Consider the situation when there are lots of protons (H^+) around, thanks to lots of carbon dioxide (CO_2).

(By the way, lots of protons [H^+] mean that the water is more acid.)

The excess of protons (H^+) combine with carbonate ions (CO_3^{2-}) – turning them back into bicarbonate (HCO_3^-) ions. The equation above has its balance altered, so it's pushed from the right-hand side towards the centre.

This means that fewer carbonate ions (CO_3^{2-}) are left in the water.

NO EFFECT FOR CENTURIES?

This effect was discussed and anticipated back in 1975 – but only from a theoretical point of view. We didn't think that having fewer carbonate ions would affect sea creatures for a century or more.

Unfortunately, we were wrong.

Late in 2012, it was reported that one particular sea creature was having its shell dissolved by the increasing acidity of the ocean.

This poor creature is the pteropod – a free-swimming sea snail that flits about thanks to wings like a butterfly's. It has a shell about 1 centimetre in diameter, and lives for two years or longer.

In the North Pacific, pteropods can make up to 60 per cent of the diet of juvenile pink salmon.

But it was at the other end of the world, down in the Antarctic, just

Adding excess carbon dioxide to seawater dramatically reduces the amount of carbonate that is available for sea creatures.

past the southern extremes of the Atlantic Ocean, that scientists found all kinds of changes happening to the sea snail. The acid ocean was dissolving its shell. One layer, called the "prismatic layer", was sometimes completely dissolved and missing. Deeper layers in the shell were now partially exposed, and the fundamental calcium carbonate matrix was increasingly porous. Overall, the shell of the pteropod was now very fragile, because it was being dissolved by the more acidic ocean.

This happened as a direct result of humans making the oceans of the world more acid.

Now, why did this first start happening in the cold Antarctic? The answer is that the chemical changes that lead to the unavailability of calcium carbonate are more extreme at low temperatures. As an example, gases (such as carbon dioxide) dissolve better in cold water – and not so well in warm water.

MORE PROBLEMS...

So the coral reefs in warmer waters are safe for a while – although scientists have been seeing less calcification on various coral reefs. But when the coral reefs get more severely affected, there will be a problem for us humans. You see, about one quarter of all the fish eaten by one billion people in Asia come from coral reefs.

In 2012, researchers at Oregon State University linked the recent increase in ocean acidity to a collapse in oyster seed production. The site was a commercial oyster hatchery in Oregon. The growth of the oyster larvae had dropped so much that the hatchery was no longer economically viable. Dr Burke Hales said, "This is one of the first times that we have been able to show how ocean acidification affects oyster larval development at a critical life stage. The predicted rise of atmospheric CO_2 in the next two to three decades may push oyster larval growth to lower than the break-even point in terms of production."

> The rate at which the oceans are getting more acidic is the fastest in the past 300 million years.

Down in the Antarctic, the pteropod is the main sea creature that makes calcium carbonate. In fact, these sea butterflies account for some 12 per cent of the entire flux of carbon on our whole planet.

The problem is that 12 per cent is a huge amount for one single creature to deal with. What if the pteropods die out? What happens to the carbon that they used to deal with? We don't know, but we'll find out over time.

Another problem is that Ocean Acidification will influence the biochemical dynamics of many other elements, such as iron, phosphorus, zinc, vanadium, chromium and so on. These elements are essential in the ocean's Web of Life – sometimes in ways that we don't yet understand.

CANARY?

Suppose that we continue with Business as Usual, and continue to dump carbon dioxide into the atmosphere until the end of the 21st century. If we foolishly follow this path, it's projected that the oceans will get more acidic, dropping another 0.3 or 0.4 points down the pH scale.

The oceans haven't been this acid for the past 40 million years. Furthermore, the rate at which the oceans are getting more acidic is the fastest in the past 300 million years. A small number of sea creatures will undoubtedly flourish, but the vast majority will suffer.

Perhaps this little sea butterfly is like the canary that olden-day miners used to carry underground to warn them when the air was bad.

The trouble is that when the canary started to croak, the miners could run out of the mine – to safety. In our case, if the sea butterflies die, where do we run to?

Another planet?

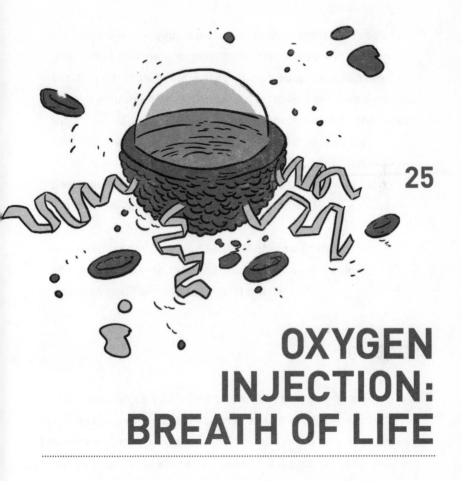

25

OXYGEN INJECTION: BREATH OF LIFE

The word "resuscitation" literally means to revive somebody and to bring them back from unconsciousness or impending death. Resuscitating sick people has been part of our human medical history for thousands of years. But now there's a new way to resuscitate someone – injecting oxygen directly into their bloodstream. This technique can keep you alive, even if you can't breathe.

Blood *Not* a Liquid?

Blood does so many different things that
I no longer think of it as a liquid.

Besides supplying oxygen, blood also supplies nutrients and
removes waste. It's also a messenger (carrying hormones,
warnings of tissue damage, etc.), and part of the immune
system (detecting invaders, transporting both immune system
cells and chemicals, etc). It helps regulate your temperature
and your acid–base balance. Blood also has "hydraulic
functions" in the penis, clitoris and nose. And let's not forget
that in a wound the blood at the surface will "coagulate",
to stop the rest of the blood from leaking out.

After I went to Medical School, I began to think of
"blood" as an incredibly complex organ that happens
to take the form of about five litres of liquid.

BLOOD 101

Blood is about 55 per cent salty water and about 45 per cent cells.

The salty water (the 55 per cent) is called "blood plasma". It's
straw-yellow in colour and comprises about 92 per cent water and
8 per cent other chemicals. Most of these are proteins, but there
are also smaller amounts of glucose, iron, hormones, fatty acids,
dissolved carbon dioxide and oxygen, and the like.

The cells (the other 45 per cent of your blood) are mostly red
blood cells, with much smaller numbers of white blood cells and
platelets. The red blood cells are jam packed with an iron-containing
protein called haemoglobin. Haemoglobin chemically combines with,
and carries, 98.5 per cent of blood's oxygen – the remaining 1.5 per

cent is dissolved in the blood plasma. (So haemoglobin is about 70 times better at carrying oxygen than the blood plasma). Normally haemoglobin picks up the oxygen as it passes through the lungs, and then delivers it to where it's needed.

In the average adult, your arterial blood is delivering about 950 to 1150 millilitres of oxygen per minute. This arterial blood is carrying about 98 to 99 per cent of the oxygen that it can potentially take – so we say that it's about 98 to 99 per cent saturated. At rest, you use about 200 to 250 millilitres of oxygen per minute, and so your veins are carrying about 750 to 900 millilitres of oxygen per minute. The blood in your veins on its way back to the lungs (to get reoxygenated) is about 75 per cent saturated.

But this is when you're at rest. What happens when you exercise? A trained athlete performing sustained exercise can use so much oxygen in the muscles that (at least for a short time) the venous blood saturation can drop below 15 per cent, and arterial saturation can drop to 95 per cent.

In general, oxygen saturation less than 90 per cent in the arteries is considered dangerous, and less than 30 per cent can be rapidly fatal.

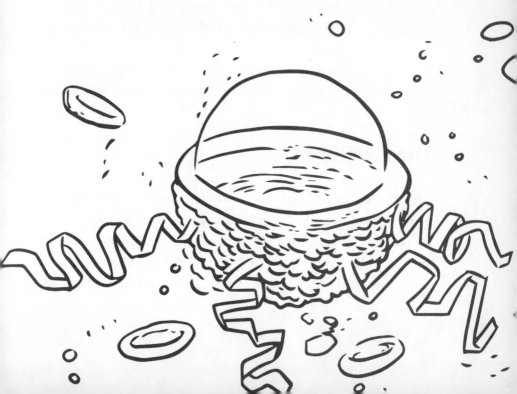

Other Oxygenation Methods

In the late 19th century, Dr John Harvey Kellogg (yup, the Corn Flakes dude) experimented with oxygen enemas (yup, oxygen gas bubbled into the bowel via the anus). Oxygen did cross the gut wall into the bloodstream – but would then coalesce into bigger bubbles and cause potentially lethal pulmonary emboli. This "bottom" method bypasses the lungs.

In the 1989 James Cameron movie *The Abyss*, US Navy SEALs have to deal with both a sunken US Ballistic Missile Submarine and NTIs (Non-Terrestrial Intelligence). They are at very great depths, so they breathe a special liquid loaded with oxygen.

Back in 1966, a mouse (which is, of course, much, much smaller than a human) survived for eight hours breathing perfluorocarbon, an oxygen-rich liquid. However, there are still many technical and physiological problems involved with breathing liquids, including short storage life, high viscosity, very high mass of liquid to be moved in and out of the lungs, difficulty in removing carbon dioxide, heart attacks and strokes, and adverse immune system reactions. Most of all, successfully breathing a liquid that is loaded with oxygen relies on functioning lungs.

THE EMERGENCY

Let's suppose you've been in some kind of terrible accident (say, an earthquake or a car crash) and your airway is blocked.

Your heart can still beat, but no new air is getting into your lungs – so your blood is not picking up any oxygen. By an amazing and lucky coincidence, the Emergency People happen to be with you

– but it's going to take them 15 minutes to open up your airway. You're going to be dead within 4 minutes unless you can get oxygen some other way.

This is exactly where this new resuscitation invention steps in. The Emergency People grab a bottle of a special liquid, and start injecting it into your bloodstream. This liquid magically (OK, scientifically) supplies your red blood cells with oxygen. It keeps you oxygenated and alive until the Emergency People can fix whatever is blocking your airway. They still have to fix everything else in less than 15 minutes, but that gives them a lot longer than the 4 minutes they would have otherwise had.

So, with this new oxygen-carrying liquid, you can do without your lungs – for about 15 minutes. So long as your heart is beating, the circulating blood will carry the oxygen it gets from the special liquid that was injected into your bloodstream.

But, in the same way that you have to keep breathing all the time, the special liquid has to be continuously injected. The moment that the emergency team stops injecting this oxygen-carrying liquid, your blood will rapidly deoxygenate.

LOM = LIPIDIC OXYGEN-CONTAINING MICROPARTICLES

This magical product was developed by a team at the Boston Children's Hospital. It goes under the fancy name of Lipidic Oxygen-Containing Microparticles. In plain English, it's a tiny ball of high-pressure oxygen, surrounded by a very thin wall of fat.

Dr John Kheir and his team experimented with many different types of fats until they came up with a combination that worked. They blasted high-pressure soundwaves through these fats while they were in an oxygen atmosphere. The fats spontaneously formed into hollow balls containing oxygen at high pressure. The team then poured water over the hollow balls and so now they had their "special" liquid. This liquid had about 10 billion oxygen-containing balls of fat per litre.

These hollow balls are around 2 to 4 microns in diameter. (A micron is one millionth of a metre, and your hair is around 50 to 70 microns in diameter). The thickness of this wall of fat is one thousandth of the diameter of the hollow sphere, or about two billionths of a metre.

Because these hollow balls are so tiny, the oxygen inside them is at very high pressure. There is a lot of oxygen stored in all of these hollow balls. There are about 10 billion of these oxygen-containing hollow balls per litre of liquid.

After the team had manufactured a bottle of the special liquid, they tested it on themselves.

Let me quote Dr John Kheir: "We drew each other's blood, mixed it in a test tube with the microparticles, and watched blue blood turn immediately red, right before our eyes." Now, of course, deoxygenated blood is not really blue, it's more of a dark, dark red – but you get the idea.

Their second study was done with anaesthetised rabbits. The team blocked the airways of the rabbits. If they had done nothing else, the animals would have been dead within minutes. But instead, they infused their oxygen-containing microparticles into the bloodstream of the rabbits – which stayed alive for another 15 minutes.

The microparticles, once they are transferred to the bloodstream, give up their oxygen within a few seconds to the nearest deoxygenated red blood cells.

NOTHING IS PERFECT

Now while this magic oxygen-containing liquid works, it is not a perfect solution to the problem of a blocked airway.

First, the microparticles come in a liquid. The heart pumps liquid blood around the body. There's a limit to how much liquid you can add to this circulatory system before the heart gets overloaded. This limit is reached in about 15 minutes. And once you stop adding the microparticles, you stop adding oxygen.

Second, while the microparticles deliver oxygen, they do not remove the carbon dioxide you continue to generate. The carbon dioxide dissolves in the blood plasma and slowly makes it more acid. But this won't be a major problem within 15 minutes.

Third, the team has not fully worked out what happens to the fats as they break down. They know that once it is empty of oxygen, this hollow sphere of fat breaks down by buckling and folding itself into millions of smaller solid balls of fat. The further breakdown of the fat needs to be better understood.

But as a simple First Aid approach, this 15-minute solution to the problem of keeping somebody supplied with oxygen while you open up their airways is terrific.

And with my crystal ball, I'd like to predict elite athletes will soon be soon queuing up to buy their own stash of this magic bottled oxygen . . . but don't hold your breath.

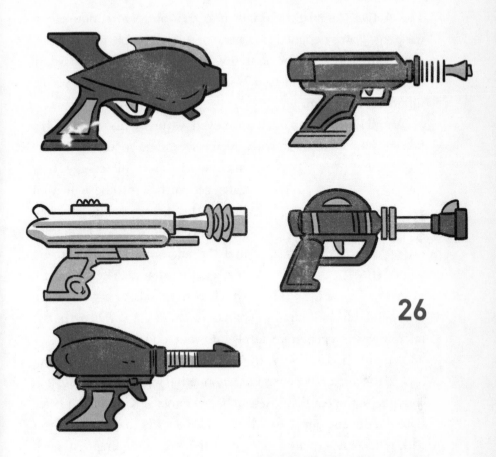

26

PAIN RAY

At first it feels like a giant invisible hairdryer is blowing hot air on you. But a few seconds later the feeling becomes so intense that you experience a burning sensation all over your skin. Welcome to the Pain Ray, or the Heat Ray, or to use the technical name, the "Microwave Directed-Energy Weapon". The military term is "Active Denial System" or "ADS".

MICROWAVES MAKE HEAT

The Active Denial System falls into the category of "non-lethal" weapons. It was designed to control or subdue people in war zones, supposedly with little or no injury. It's claimed to be less harmful than batons, rubber bullets or Tasers. It's basically just a super-powerful microwave beam.

We all know that a microwave oven warms up last night's Thai takeaway by blasting it with microwaves. The food absorbs the microwaves, and the energy they carry gets turned into heat. In your home, the power output of your microwave oven is about 1 kilowatt, and the microwaves usually have a frequency of around 2.45 gigahertz – which corresponds to a wavelength of around 122 millimetres. Thanks to this long wavelength, the microwaves can penetrate deeply into your food.

> You can get a very nasty full-thickness burn from water at the surprisingly low temperature of 55°C.

Back in the late 1980s, the US Military began thinking about how to use microwave energy as a non-lethal weapon. This research was done at the Air Force Research Laboratory at Kirtland Air Force Base in Albuquerque, New Mexico. The key was to use microwaves with a frequency of around 95 gigahertz, corresponding to a much shorter wavelength of around 3.2 millimetres. They also cranked up the power to around 1000 kilowatts. These short-wavelength microwaves penetrated the skin to a depth of only about 0.4 millimetres. Water in that thin epidermal layer of skin absorbs the microwave energy and turns it into heat energy – lots of it.

Skin Effect

A series of studies looked at how human volunteers responded
to very powerful microwave radiation at different frequencies.
These frequencies were 2.45 gigahertz (as in your home
microwave oven), 7.5, 10, 35 and 94 gigahertz. The scientists
irradiated the volunteers for 10 seconds at a time,
at one-minute intervals.

They found that as the frequency increased, more of the energy
got concentrated into an increasingly thin band in the top layer
of the skin. At 2.45 gigahertz, they needed lots of microwaves
to induce pain – 63 megawatts per square centimetre. But
at 94 gigahertz, the power needed was 14 times less –
just 4.5 megawatts per square centimetre.

This meant that if they ran their Pain Ray at 94 gigahertz, they
could generate lots more pain for the same amount of power.

WEAPONISED MICROWAVES

Luckily for the Military, we humans have a very sensitive heat
receptor in that outer layer of our skin. It's called a Thermal
Nocioceptor. From an evolutionary point of view, it's very important
that we are sensitive to heat, because our skin is so fragile. You can
get a very nasty full-thickness burn from water at the surprisingly
low temperature of 55°C. The military did not want to go this far.

The first version of the Active Denial System weapon was called
System O and was delivered in the year 2000. It worked, but it was
seriously overweight at 7.5 tonnes. The current system is lighter, but
still has to be carried by a Hummer or light truck. It looks like a
large satellite dish, produces a beam about 2 metres across and has a

range of half a kilometre – that's about 17 times the range of rubber bullets. It fires in repeated bursts, each about 3 to 5 seconds long. One advantage is that the "ammunition" is effectively unlimited.

In 2012, Spencer Ackerman, a reporter for *Wired* magazine, volunteered at a media event to stand in the beam of the Pain Ray. He said afterwards, "my shoulder and upper chest . . . felt like they were being roasted, with what can be likened to a super-hot tingling feeling". Most people can stand the beam for 3 seconds or less – and then their reflexes take over and they run away. That's what reflexes do when your skin is screaming in agony.

> At the moment, the Pain Ray machine is large and cumbersome, and it doesn't work very well when there's rain, fog, mist, snow or a dust storm.

The Active Denial System was sent to Afghanistan in 2010, but for various reasons was never used. Raytheon (the fifth largest military contractor in the world) designed and built the Active Denial System, and has built a few smaller versions – for use in prison cells, as hand-held weapons, and to be fired from aircraft.

At the moment, the Pain Ray machine is large and cumbersome. Another problem is that the Pain Ray doesn't work very well when there's rain, fog, mist, snow or a dust storm. It's also very slow to warm up. It doesn't turn on instantly like a light bulb – instead, it takes 16 hours to be fully operational from a cold start. You could keep it running all the time, but it would burn up a lot of fuel.

MICROWAVE MEETS HUMAN

The heat delivered to the skin by the Pain Ray depends on the power produced, the distance to the victim and for how long they are exposed.

So far, in controlled trials, it appears to be relatively safe. There have been only eight burn injuries from the more than 11,000 volunteers who have been exposed to the beam in experimental tests. But in one of those the power was accidentally reset to maximum, and the burns were so severe that a volunteer apparently needed skin grafts. Furthermore, a "controlled trial" is very different from "out in the field". Some people might have underlying medical conditions that could predispose them to nasty injuries.

And what about permanent injuries?

Consider an oppressive government that wants to stop a legitimate peaceful demonstration or a workers' strike – they could simply run the Pain Ray for 10 seconds, instead of 5, potentially causing severe burns.

What if the Pain Ray were used upon a crowd who simply could not leave the area because the exits were blocked? In that case you would expect that some people would be zapped by the beam several times over – possibly causing a horrible, disfiguring roasting of the skin.

And what about torture?

Overly enthusiastic police officers have been known to use Tasers over and over again on people who were already restrained and who posed no threat. If you leave enough time between exposures, the Pain Ray will cause intense distress, but won't leave any marks.

Will we be able to trust the authorities never to misuse the Pain Ray?

Maybe yes, maybe no.

But look on the bright side. When you're next at a peaceful demonstration, take last night's leftovers, just in case they pull out the Pain Ray . . .

27

PHONEY RELATIONSHIPS

I had a smartphone in the Olden Days, when they were known as "wanker phones". It was neither "smart" nor worth bragging about – it would crash during a phone call!

But I fell in love with the modern smartphone when we walked 800 kilometres across Spain on El Camino de Santiago de Compostela. It was a true technological marvel. It was my phone – plus my Spanish–English dictionary, my notebook, my camera, my GPS, and it also gave me web and email access.

A typical smartphone has four separate radio transmitter–receivers – one for voice, one for data, one for Bluetooth and another for WiFi. It can put you in contact with the whole world. But the funny thing is that your smartphone can also make your personal relationships shallow.

PERSONAL DISCUSSION

Andrew K. Pryzbylski and Netta Weinstein of the University of Essex carried out some rather neat psychological studies. I should point out that they used a "nondescript mobile phone" – which may or may not have been a modern smartphone.

In the first study, 74 participants – 26 women and 48 men – with an average age of 22 were told to "discuss an interesting event that occurred to you over the past month".

The volunteers surrendered all of their personal belongings, were randomly matched to a partner and then led to a private booth where they had 10 minutes to discuss their assigned topic. There were three pieces of furniture in the booth – two chairs and a table. Of course, they each sat in a chair.

> I know people who place their phones in the middle of the table at dinner. The first person to answer or look at their phone has to pay for the whole group.

The trick of the experiment was with what was left on the table, off to one side. In half of the discussions, it was a book and a pocket notepad. But for the other half it was a book and a mobile phone. None of the items belonged to the volunteers.

Afterwards, they separately filled out questionnaires about the connectedness of the conversation, how close a relationship they had, and their feelings of closeness during their 10-minute get-together.

In the pairs who had a phone sitting on the table, each volunteer reported a lower quality of relationship and less closeness – even though neither of them owned the phone. Despite them not consciously noticing the phone, it somehow interfered with their frankness.

Recorder?

So why were people less likely to be intimate in the presence of the mobile phone? (Did the phone register in their subconscious?)

People know that a phone can transmit live to the outside world and can record any nearby conversations. Perhaps these concepts briefly flickered into the consciousness of the participants, and made them more reticent?

TOGETHER, BUT APART

Ubiquitous mobile phones have changed our dining manners.

Think of a group of people sitting down to a meal together in a restaurant. They will be laughing and catching up on the news and swapping stories – but maybe not with the people at the same table. Often they'll ignore the people eating with them and interact with somebody else, who is somewhere else on the planet. And even if they're not chatting with somebody somewhere else, they could be checking their email, or cataloguing their photos, or checking into a Social Network.

I know people who deliberately place their phones in the middle of the table at dinner. The first person to answer or look at their phone has to pay for the whole group. Otherwise, everybody pays their share. It's interesting they have to make new rules in order to concentrate on the people they are with. But even that won't save them from the shallow talk the phone predestines them to.

Mind you, the mobile phone is a magnificent way to keep in contact and maintain some degree of personal intimacy with people you are separated from.

PERSONAL AND NON-PERSONAL DISCUSSION

The psychologists next repeated their experiment – but with a twist.

For half of the meetings, the assigned topic of conversation would be moderately intimate: discuss the "most meaningful events of the past year". For the other half, the discussion was totally casual: what did they think about plastic Christmas trees?

The volunteers were put through the same rituals sitting in a room with the three pieces of furniture – and, again, half the time there was a mobile phone on the table beside them, and the other half of the time it was replaced with a notepad.

When there was a phone present, it made no difference to the casual conversation, but a world of difference to the intimate conversation. The intimate conversation became more shallow.

But if there was no phone nearby, the intimate conversation would "help foster closeness, connectedness, interpersonal trust, and perceptions of empathy – the building blocks of relationships".

A BETTER OFFER . . .

As Helen Lee Lin wrote on *Scientific American*'s Mind Matters blog, "because of the many social, instrumental and entertainment options phones [give] us, they often divert our attention [away] from our current environment . . . phones may serve as a reminder of the wider network to which we could connect, inhibiting our ability to connect with the people right next to us."

Now, the volunteers in the study did not actively notice that there was a mobile phone nearby. But somehow, its mere presence "inhibited the development of interpersonal closeness of trust, and reduced the extent to which individuals felt empathy and understanding from their partner".

Today, over 85 per cent of the people in the world have a mobile phone. Every day, billions of conversations take place on these mobile phones. There are also billions of face-to-face conversations with a phone placed casually on a table or bar nearby. How are we to deal with the fact that these phones simultaneously "facilitate as well as disrupt human bonding and intimacy"?

The technology is new, but the problem seems to be an age-old one: "The grass looks greener on the other side". Today, our phones show us so many greener fields . . .

BTW (By The Way), if you "Liked" this article, why not Tweet the link, or Share it on Facebook . . .

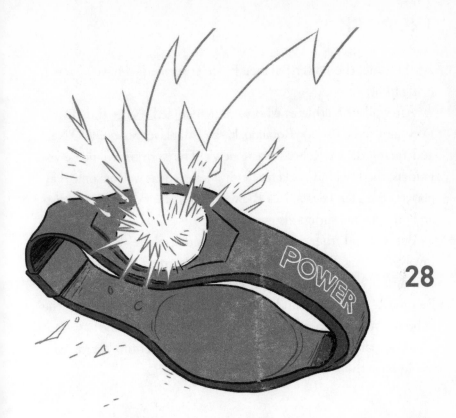

28

POWER BALANCE BRACELETS

You might remember that a long time ago in the distant past – around 2010 – a miraculous product appeared. It was supposed to improve your balance, strength and flexibility. And as "proof" that it worked, many A-list athletes wore one on a wrist – yes, let's think back to the Power Balance Bracelet.

However, thanks to excellent work by Richard Saunders of the Australian Skeptics, the bracelets were shown to be totally fraudulent. By 2011, sales across the world had collapsed.

THE PITCH

At the time, the Power Balance Bracelet seemed to have so much going for it.

After all, the athletes who wore it included soccer stars David Beckham and Cristiano Ronaldo, basketball player Shaquille O'Neal and racing driver Rubens Barrichello. The sprinter Mark Lewis-Francis, the England cricketer Kevin Pietersen, as well as some AFL players (Brendan Fevola, Jack Riewoldt, etc.), Tour de France cyclists and professional surfers also wore them.

But beyond the ringing endorsements, there was "science" involved. This Power Balance product worked because of the wonderful "Mylar hologram". It was claimed to put you in Cosmic Resonance with the Fundamental Vibration of our planet – the Schumann Resonance at 7.83 Hertz (or cycles per second).

With (paid) testimonials and fancy "pseudo-scientific" words, who would have thought it could possibly be a fraud?

POWER BALANCE BRACELET 101

To the naked eye, the Power Balance Bracelet was just a rubber band bracelet with a shiny plastic disc. (Actually, there were two products, both a touch pricey – the pendant necklace at \$95 and the much more popular wristband at \$60.)

According to the marketers, it was so much more. The rubber band was actually a "surgical grade silicone wristband". And the shiny disc was not just a bit of flat plastic glued onto a rubber band. It was a hologram, "based on the idea of optimizing the body's natural body flow, similar to concepts behind many Eastern philosophies. The hologram is designed to respond to the natural energy field of the body. The Mylar material at the core . . . has been treated with energy waves at specific frequencies . . ."

That hodge-podge of "sciencey" words all jumbled together was meant to impress the average person on the street.

Like all good Sales Pitches, there is a small element of truth buried in the flim-flam.

Yes, the human brain does have "electrical waves" running through it. (Maybe that's what the marketing meant by an "energy field".) And there really is a standing wave that runs through the Earth's atmosphere, which is called the "Schumann Resonance" – and it has a frequency of 7.83 Hertz. And if you really want to get down to it, the Earth under our feet hums with seismic waves running through it.

But are they linked in any way whatsoever? If you wear a bit of shiny plastic glued onto a rubber band, will you achieve Cosmic Consciousness? And, more basically, can the Power Balance Bracelet give you more powerful muscles, better balance and flexibility? The answer to all of these questions: nope.

Let's splash through the waves that run through not only the Power Balance hologram, but our brain, our Planet's atmosphere, and also through the Planet beneath our feet.

POWER BALANCE FREQUENCIES AND WAVES

Imagine that you blow across the mouth of an empty bottle. Suddenly you can hear the natural resonant frequency of the closed space inside that bottle. It's an audio frequency in the range that your ears can hear.

The formula is straightforward:

$$\text{Speed} = \text{Wavelength} \times \text{Frequency}$$

For sound waves, the Speed is about 300 metres per second, and the height of the bottle (the Wavelength) is about 30 centimetres. That gives you a Frequency of around 1000 Hertz – easy to hear.

For electromagnetic waves (radio waves, light waves, Schumann Resonance), the Speed is about a million times faster – about 300,000 kilometres per second. The hologram on the Power Balance products is about 1.5 centimetres across – the Wavelength. That gives it a natural resonant frequency of about 1000 million million Hertz.

BRAIN WAVES

So what about the frequencies beating in the human brain?

Our brain has about 86 billion neurons (plus or minus 10 per cent). These neurons are all electrically active – but at various frequencies. If you place a net of a few dozen sensing electrodes on the scalp, you can't pick up the activity of an individual neuron. But you can pick up the activity of several million of them, if they are all beating in synchrony.

> The frequencies of the Power Balance hologram and the brain are different by several hundred million million times.

The first fact to realise is that the brain doesn't vibrate only and exactly at 7.83 Hertz (to match the Schumann Resonance). It has electrical waves of hundreds of different frequencies running through it. There are six major subdivisions of these waves. They are the Alpha Waves (about 8 to 13 cycles per second, or 8 to 13 Hertz), Beta Waves (13 to 30 Hertz), Gamma Waves (30 to 100+ Hertz), Delta Waves (up to 4 Hertz), Theta Waves (4 to 8 Hertz) and Mu Waves (8 to 13 Hertz).

Second, it's complicated. The "normal" EEG changes if you are awake or asleep. And if you are asleep, the EEG pattern changes depending on which one of the five stages of sleep you are in. It's also affected by anaesthetics, opiates, benzodiazepines, if you are in a state of cognitive decline or a coma or just plain tired, and any one of a dozen or so brain diseases.

EEG 101

Back in 1924, the German psychiatrist Hans Berger recorded the first human electroencephalograph (EEG). He placed pairs of electrodes on a patient's scalp, and recorded the electrical signal from each set of electrodes.

Since then, more advanced diagnostic imaging technologies (Computed Tomography (CT), functional Magnetic Resonance Imaging (fMRI), Positron Emission Tomography (PET), etc.) have been introduced, but the old-fashioned EEG still has some advantages. It's cheap, silent, doesn't involve exposure to intense magnetic fields or radioactive materials, and can detect brain activity on the time scale of thousandths of a second, rather than seconds.

So it's still used for distinguishing different types of epileptic seizures, for monitoring a coma, as an adjunct test of brain death and so on.

POWER BALANCE AND BRAIN

As we saw earlier, the Power Balance hologram has a natural resonance of about 1000 million million Hertz. The human brain has hundreds of different resonances running though it, covering frequencies from 2 to 100 Hertz.

The frequencies of the Power Balance hologram and the brain are different by several hundred million million times. So, they are not even close to each other.

SEISMIC WAVES

Over the past few decades, the geologists and physicists have discovered that the Earth beneath our feet vibrates with a mysterious Hum (or frequency).

Our Planet is mostly jelly-like. The solid crust is just a very thin layer, making up a mere 1 per cent of our planet's structure.

Our Planet's depth is a bit less than 6400 kilometres from the surface down to the centre. The first 50 or so kilometres are solid rock. Underneath that is "molten" rock down to about 2890 kilometres. Then there's an Outer Core of liquid iron reaching from 2890 to 5100 kilometres, which surrounds the Inner Core, a solid ball of iron.

By the 1980s, the geophysicists found (with sensitive seismometers and powerful computers) that the Earth was vibrating – even when there had been no recent major earthquake to give it a mighty blow. But they made a mistake and incorrectly guessed that these vibrations had been set off by a few tiny earthquakes that were too small to notice.

Finally, in 1997, two Japanese geophysicists discovered the Hum. Naoki Suda and Kazunari Nawa had read a paper by a Japanese theoretician, Naoki Kobayashi, who had mathematically predicted that movements of the Earth's atmosphere should make the Earth wobble like jelly. They did the obvious thing that no other scientists had done before them. They first looked at the records from the seismographic stations that had the lowest background noise levels, and then analysed the rare days when no earthquakes had happened nearby. Then they applied their "frequency-chasing" computer programs to look for the oscillations within the Earth. They had found the "Hum".

Once Suda and Nawa had discovered the Hum, the rest of the scientific community tried to work out what caused it. Even today, we're not 100 per cent sure. There are many contenders, including the atmosphere (as postulated by Hobayashi), the pounding of the surf along the beaches and slow tidal movements of the oceans. At the moment, probably the best contender is that the interaction of ocean waves over the shallow continental shelves drives the "Hum" of our Planet.

By the way, the entire power of the Hum over our whole Planet is only about 500 watts – not even enough to run a microwave oven.

POWER BALANCE AND EARTH?

But what about the frequencies of the Hum being exactly lined up with the frequencies of the Power Balance hologram? Nope.

The Hum is not one single pure note, but about 50 different notes, squashed into a bandwidth of about two octaves. But these two octaves are far below our range of hearing. The lowest frequency we humans can hear is about 20 Hertz. The Earth's Hum frequencies are between two and seven *thousandths* of a Hertz – or, in musical terms, about 16 octaves below middle C. In plain English, they're about a million million million times lower than any of the frequencies in the Power Balance hologram.

> By the 1980s, the geophysicists found that the Earth was vibrating – even when there had been no recent major earthquake to give it a mighty blow.

Furthermore, this sound is not particularly pleasant or enlightening. When you shift it upwards 16 octaves into the audible band that our ears can hear, it sounds like a bored person banging a garbage bin lid very loudly.

SCHUMANN RESONANCE

But what about the Schumann Resonance in our atmosphere? Let's go back to the example of blowing across the mouth of an empty bottle.

We'll make two changes. First, let's use electromagnetic radiation, not sound waves. Second, let's change our closed space from a bottle to the Earth's atmosphere. The atmosphere wraps right around our planet – all the way from the ground up to the bottom of the ionosphere (which begins some 50 kilometres above the ground).

Ionosphere

The ionosphere is a region surrounding our Planet. It reaches, in several sub-layers, from about 50 to 1000 kilometres above the ground.

It's called the *io*nosphere because it's full of *ions*.

You might remember from high school that atoms resemble mini solar systems. They have a nucleus in the middle (corresponding to the Sun) with electrons (corresponding to the planets) orbiting around it. When you rip an electron off, or add an extra electron, what's left is called an "ion".

Once you get higher than 50 kilometres above the ground, the atmosphere becomes very thin and dilute. The atoms are (relatively speaking) a long way apart.

Down at ground level, the Sun's radiation has been much weakened. Most of it has been absorbed by the atoms in the atmosphere. But near the top of the atmosphere, very little of the Sun's power has been absorbed.

As a result, much, much more of the Sun's powerful radiations (ultraviolet, X-ray, etc.) can hit these atoms. These radiations can rip one or more electrons away from these atoms, turning them into charged ions. Normally these ions would run into an atom almost immediately and lose their charge, and turn back into an atom. But these atoms at the top of the atmosphere are a lot further apart. So the ions can travel for a much longer distance and time before they turn back into atoms. That's why this layer is called the ionosphere – it's full of conductive, electrically charged ions.

Because they are charged, these large numbers of ions can affect electromagnetic radiation. In the old days before satellite communication, the various layers in the ionosphere were used for many types of radio communications over long distances.

These different layers in the ionosphere can reflect or trap electromagnetic radiation underneath them. So you and I can think of the Earth's atmosphere between the ground and the ionosphere as being a "closed cavity" for some frequencies of electromagnetic radiation. But the physicists think of it as a "closed waveguide".

So potentially our atmosphere would resonate – if there was something to excite it. In the case of our bottle, the excitation energy was in the moving air that our mouth blew across the top of the bottle. In the case of our atmosphere, the excitation energy comes from lightning. There are about 50 to 100 lightning bolts each second, averaged across the planet. They happen mostly in Asia, Africa and South America.

The circumference of our planet (about 40,000 kilometres) is our wavelength. That means that electromagnetic radiation will have a certain natural resonant frequency – about 7.83 Hertz. On one hand, that frequency is roughly one third of the lowest frequency that we can hear with our ears – tantalisingly close. But we do not have any organs in our body that can pick up that frequency in the electromagnetic spectrum.

> The brain, the Earth and the Earth's atmosphere each have their own individual collections of various waves with many different frequencies.

This natural resonant frequency for electromagnetic radiation of our atmosphere is called the Schumann Resonance. It is named after the German physicist Winfried Otto Schumann. Besides the fundamental radio frequency of 7.83 Hertz, there are also progressively weaker higher harmonics at 14.3 Hertz, 20.8 Hertz, 27.3 Hertz and so on.

These frequencies have no spiritual significance. They are simply related to the Speed of Light and the circumference of our planet.

COMPLETE RUBBISH

So what's the chance that the Power Balance Bracelets could resonate with "stuff" inside and around us?

From a Practical point of view, none.

All the double-blind tests (where neither the person wearing the Power Balance Bracelet nor the person testing them knew if they were wearing them) showed no improvement in power, balance or flexibility.

From a Theoretical point of view, none.

The brain, the Earth beneath our feet, and the Earth's atmosphere each has its own individual collections of various waves with many different frequencies. These waves are of many different types – so there's no simple way to "harmonise" or link them together.

Earthquakes in the ground produce different types of seismic waves – longitudinal P-Waves, transverse S-Waves and Surface Waves. The electroencephalograph measures changes in voltage caused by ions flowing into or out of neurons in the brain. The Schumann Resonance in the atmosphere is electromagnetic radiation trapped between the ground and the base of the ionosphere, and set off by continual barrage of 50 to 100 lightning bolts to second.

None of these natural frequencies (the brain, the Earth, the atmosphere) resonate with each other, or with the Power Balance Bracelet.

From a Legal point of view, none.

In December 2010, the Australian Consumer and Competition Commission (ACCC) "ordered Power Balance Australia to cease marketing its wristbands with claims of boosted sporting performance, and demanded they refund people already duped by the purported benefits". The chairman of the ACCC at the time, Graeme Samuel, said, "You could buy rubber bands from the newsagent and have a fresh one every day of the year".

Since then, the makers of the Power Balance Bracelets have been forced to stop marketing them in this way in the USA, Italy, the Netherlands and elsewhere.

Today, the only benefit of the Power Balance Bracelet is that it lets you easily recognise gullible people . . .

Prediction

Way back in 1999, I received a panicked email from a listener to my Triple J radio show. He had just received a chain email (equivalent to the old printed chain letters of the past) and was convinced there was no point in living any more.

This email is a good example of totally unproven claims, using lots of "scientific" words to try to gain some credibility. They still circulate today.

Let me quote some of the email, with my comments in italics.

The resonance of Earth (Schumann Resonance) has been 7.8 Hertz for thousands of years. *Yes, correct.* Since 1980 it has risen to over 12 Hertz. *Incorrect – it has not risen since 1980.* This means that 16 hours now equates to a 24-hour day. *Incorrect – the days are still 24 hours long.* Time is speeding up. *Incorrect – time is still the same.*

When the Earth's resonance frequency reaches 13 cycles per second, we will be at a Zero Point magnetic field. *Incorrect – the Schumann Resonance frequency is related only to the Earth's circumference and the Speed of Light. These don't change, so the Schumann Resonance frequency doesn't change. And even if the Schumann Resonance frequency did change, this would not affect the Earth's Magnetic Field.*

The Earth will be stopped, and in 2 or 3 days it will start revolving once again, but in the opposite direction. *Incorrect – the Earth did not stop and then start rotating in the opposite direction.*

Our DNA is being reprogrammed from the Universe (as predicted in the Mayan Prophecy), changing from 2-strand back to 12-strand DNA. *Incorrect – our DNA still has two strands. And the Mayans did not predict that the Universe would reprogram our DNA.*

Eyes will become cat-like in order to adjust to the new atmosphere and light conditions. *Incorrect – my eyes are still the same shape.*

All children born after 1998 will probably be telepathic at birth. *(From the date, I guess the email had been circulating for a while.) Incorrect – telepathy has still not been proven to exist.*

The Zero Point flip will probably catapult Earth into the 4th dimension. *Incorrect – we're still here.* Once there, everything we think or desire will instantly manifest. *Incorrect – I think of dark chocolate, but it refuses to materialise for me.* This includes the powerful emotions of love and fear. *Incorrect.*

The Mayan Calendar predicted all the changes that are occurring now. *Incorrect – a calendar can't predict anything except the days of the week.* It infers that as we enter into the new millennium, we will discard our obsolete solid-state-of-the-art 20th century technology. *Incorrect – we're still using solid state-of-the-art technology.* We will invent new devices which employ the vibrations of universal fields. *Incorrect – I can't even conceive what these "universal fields" might be.* By 2012 we will have entered into the 5th Dimension (after the flip into the 4th Dimension at Zero Point). *Incorrect – it's after 2012, and I'm still not in either the 4th or 5th Dimensions.*

Once you've read a few of these New Age "predictions", and then waited long enough to have seen how spectacularly incorrect they were, you begin to see through them. They rely on a continual supply of naïve folk.

As an aside, as part of the Mayan End of the World that was supposed to happen (rather inconveniently) just two shopping days before Christmas 2012, the planet Nibiru was supposed to swing past Earth and cause mayhem. The videos, which you can see on YouTube, have been rather clumsily re-edited to change the date of Universal Mayhem from 2012 to 2032.

And so it goes . . .

29

PSYCHOPATH WISDOM

If you did a random word association on the noun "psychopath", the grim words "serial killer" would probably appear somewhere on your list. (A good example is Dexter, the fictional Miami Police Forensics Officer who just happens to be a serial killer.) But serial killers are not the only psychopaths in our society. Many of our politicians and heroes have psychopathic tendencies – or, to be more accurate, *share* some of the same characteristics. That means that the psychopath who could cheerfully burn down your house is similar in many ways to the hero who would rescue your loved ones from the same burning home.

HISTORY OF PSYCHOPATHS

The word "psychopath" was first used in 1885. It comes from the Greek roots "psyche" meaning "mind" or "mental" and "pathos" meaning "feeling" or "suffering".

About 1 per cent of us are true psychopaths, two-thirds of whom are male. Another 10 to 15 per cent of us are in the "almost psychopathic" category.

One of the earliest appraisals of psychopathy was by the ancient Greek philosopher Theophrastus, about 2300 years ago. In his book *The Characters* he carefully lists some 30 Moral Temperaments. One of these he calls "The Unscrupulous Man" who will, according to Theophrastus, "go and borrow more money from a creditor he has yet to pay back". The Unscrupulous Man has more than one of the characteristics that psychopaths have.

EMOTIONAL CHARACTERISTICS OF PSYCHOPATHS

There are many different characteristics associated with psychopathy. On the scary side, they include having virtually no conscience, no impulse control, no guilt, no empathy and no remorse. Psychopaths are also very egocentric, very dishonest, virtually immune to anxiety and both callous and ruthless. They are very happy to take risks, and tend to have a grandiose sense of self-worth.

On the upside, psychopaths are quite mentally and physically fearless, can focus really well, are strong-minded and are superficially charming.

As a result, they are very persuasive and very skilled at manipulating others. For example, according to Dr Stephen Porter in 2009, psychopaths have "a great proficiency in persuading parole boards to release them into the community".

PHYSICAL CHARACTERISTICS OF PSYCHOPATHS

Surprisingly, the emotional characteristics of psychopathy seem to be linked to some physical attributes.

Suppose you subject people to an unpleasantly loud noise. "Regular" people get upset, but psychopaths do not.

"Regular" people blink when startled, and do so more when they are in a threatening environment. But a psychopath does not blink more.

Suppose you are reading both emotionally charged words ("kill", "torture", "joy", etc.) and neutral words ("table", "plate", etc). "Regular" people take longer to process the emotionally charged words, while psychopaths process both neutral words and emotionally charged words at the same speed.

Psychopathy seems to be linked to a poor sense of smell. One study of 79 non-criminal psychopaths living in the community tested their sense of smell. They were offered 16 pens (Sniffin' Sticks) that carried 16 different odours such as leather, orange and coffee. They could register that an odour was present. But they could not correctly identify it, and could not easily tell the difference between one scent and another.

> "Regular" people blink when startled, and do so more when they are in a threatening environment. But a psychopath does not blink more.

This poor sense of smell seems to point a finger at a part of the brain called the Orbito-Frontal Complex. Not only does it process smells, it is also involved in controlling impulses and in planning. It might function differently in psychopaths.

Psychopaths and Athletes

Psychopaths share seven characteristics with great athletes.

They are cool under pressure, and won't crumble under the strain of a tough match.

They can focus mightily to the exclusion of all else – shame about the family and friends, though.

They are ruthless and can finish the job under virtually any circumstances.

They have a Vulnerability Radar that can sense weakness in their opponents.

They are mentally tough and can come back from severe setbacks in their career.

Both psychopaths and great athletes have charm and charisma.

Finally, they both can live totally in the present. This means they are not bothered by something bad (for example, a missed shot) that happened a little earlier.

PSYCHOPATHS IN SOCIETY

What if you have some, but not all, of the characteristics of a psychopath? After all, some of these characteristics can be both acceptable and desirable.

It's very useful for politicians to have one characteristic possessed by psychopaths – "Fearless Dominance". This involves a total lack of apprehension or concern or worry about social and physical situations that you and I would probably be scared of. One study found a higher level of Fearless Dominance in US Presidents.

> It's very useful for politicians to have one characteristic possessed by psychopaths – "Fearless Dominance".

The so-called "Hero Populations" are those who work in the military, law enforcement, rescue services and so on. These "heroes" also have some of the characteristics of psychopaths – immunity from stress, ability to focus, social dominance and fearlessness. But, on the other hand, they do not carry other psychopathic tendencies such as lack of conscience, antisocial behaviour, impulsivity and narcissism.

Back in 1982, the psychologist D.T. Lykken said that psychopaths and heroes are "twigs on the same genetic branch".

TYPES OF PSYCHOPATHS

Consider a person who has several psychopathic traits. Now factor in the other characteristics of intelligence and a tendency to violence.

This gives you four possible results.

If you are nonviolent and not particularly smart, you'll probably end up as some kind of petty criminal – maybe a burglar.

The second option is that you are violent, but not particularly intelligent. In this scenario, you could end up as an enforcer or a low-level hood.

Things change when you add intelligence to the mix.

In the third scenario, if you are both intelligent and violent on top of your psychopathic tendencies, you could end up as a criminal mastermind – or working in the Special Forces.

But if you're psychopathic, intelligent and non-violent, you could be a "hero", or a surgeon, a lawyer or head of a big corporation. In 2006, P. Babbiak and Robert D. Hare referred to psychopaths in business settings as "Snakes in Suits".

So just when you finally get your head around having to look out for Wolves in Sheep's Clothing, you have to push it one step further to see the Snake in a Suit. But at least you'll know that the Snake in a Suit will be up high, not low to the ground . . .

How to Measure Psychopathy

In 1980 Robert D. Hare, a psychologist at the University of British Columbia in Vancouver, developed the Psychopath Checklist (PCL) that assesses the emotional deficits that underlie psychopathy. In 1991, he modified it into the currently used Revised Psychopath Checklist (PCL-R).

Psychopathic Customs Officers

A slightly psychopathic customs officer might be superior at finding smugglers carrying contraband.

In one study Dr Kevin Dutton, a research psychologist from Oxford University, gave one of five students a scarlet handkerchief to hide on their person. That student was also given £100 to keep – but only if they could successfully hide the scarlet handkerchief.

The five students had to enter the classroom through a door, walk across a small elevated stage and then leave through another door. Watching them were 30 other students. Some of the 30 ranked high in psychopathy, while others ranked low. The students with psychopathic tendencies could find the person with the scarlet handkerchief 70 per cent of the time. The "regular" students achieved 30 per cent accuracy.

It appears that psychopaths can "see" things that the rest of us cannot. For example, one psychopathic serial killer said that he picked his potential victims by "how they walked". So while being able to see the person's weakness would be useful to a predatory psychopath, it would also be useful for customs agents at airports.

30

WASTED FOOD – FROM FARM TO FORK TO LANDFILL

On average, we humans waste about 40 per cent of our food on its journey from the farm to our fork. It never reaches a human stomach. Worldwide, we produce about four billion tonnes of food each year – and toss out about 1.2 to 2 billion tonnes of it. That's 170 to 280 kilograms per person. We actually throw out more food than the average person's own body weight – two to five times more. Each year, Americans throw out food worth US$135 billion.

But generating food is expensive in ways other than cash. As an example of the enormous cost of growing food, in the USA farmers use about 50 per cent of the country's total surface area and about 80 per cent of their fresh water to make food. Furthermore, agriculture uses up a massive 10 per cent of the total US Energy Budget.

Plants are not very economical at turning the energy in sunlight into stored energy – they do it at less than 2 per cent efficiency. Then the overall or cumulative efficiency gets even lower when we feed these plants to animals. Cows turn plants into beef with only a 5 to 10 per cent efficiency, while chickens are a little higher at 10 to 15 per cent. There's another loss when we then eat the cow or chicken and convert it into human energy and mass.

The energy at the base of this system (photosynthesis) comes for free, from the Sun. But we also use fossil fuel to help produce our food (tractors, cooling, processing, transport, etc). The energy used to produce food is much greater than the energy that ends up inside the food on our plate. Typically, the US "expends roughly 10 units of fossil energy to produce one unit of food energy" – which works out to about 10 per cent of the total US Energy Budget. While the average ratio is 10 to 1, it varies from 3 to 1 for edible plants to about 35 to 1 for grain-fed beef.

That 10 per cent of the total US Energy Budget is split between 2 per cent for Agriculture, 1 per cent for Food Processing and Manufacturing, 2 per cent for Food Transportation and 5 per cent for Food Packaging, Preparation, Refrigeration, Handling, Sales and Services.

Water

We need lots of water to produce food. The water is not permanently lost once it's used – after all, it will eventually fall as rain somewhere on the planet, thanks to the Water Cycle. But in the short term, it's taken out of the water capacity of a local area.

I was saddened to discover that my favourite food, chocolate, is the thirstiest. Here is a table of how much water is needed to produce 1 kilogram of various agricultural products.

Foodstuff	Water (litres)
Chocolate	17,196
Beef	15,415
Sheep meat	10,412
Pork	5988
Butter	5553
Chicken meat	4325
Cheese	3178
Rice	2497
Bread	1608
Wine	436
Potato	287
Cabbage	237
Tomato	214
Tea	108

The surface area of Planet Earth is about 510 million square kilometres. About 149 million square kilometres is land – the rest is water. (So, yes, the name of our planet is wrong: it would be more accurately called Planet Water.)

But only about 100 million square kilometres can support productive biomass for agriculture. We are already using about half of that for food production – about 49 million square kilometres.

The area of land used for human habitation is much smaller again – only about 0.3 million square kilometres – just a little larger than Victoria.

LOST WHERE?

There are five major steps in the Food Chain where food is wasted.

Waste starts with Production Losses, then Post-Harvest, Handling and Storage Losses, followed by Processing and Packaging Losses. It moves along to Distribution and Retail Losses, and finishes up with Consumer Losses (which includes out-of-home consumption).

Surprisingly, both poor and wealthy countries lose roughly the same amount of food per person per year – but for very different reasons.

POOR COUNTRIES

In poor countries food is wasted at many stages. But, overall, there are more losses at the farmer–producer end of the chain.

Sometimes food cannot be harvested, or it cannot be transported to storage areas. If it does make it into storage, it might spoil before it gets to market. "Cold storage" means that food can be stored for much longer – but it's not very common in poor countries.

And, of course, if a poor country is at war, that makes everything worse.

WEALTHY COUNTRIES

If we take the USA, Canada, Australia and New Zealand as examples, on average we waste about 52 per cent of our fruit and vegetables, 50 per cent of our seafood, 38 per cent of our grain products, 22 per cent of our meat and 20 per cent of our milk. As a specific example, the USA wastes enough food each day to fill the famous 90,000-seat Rose Bowl football stadium to the brim. At the same time, one in six Americans lacks a secure supply of food to their table.

In wealthy countries, food wastage follows a slightly different script from poor countries' food losses. In wealthy countries, the losses tend to happen further along the supply chain. While some of the problems occur in both poor countries and in wealthy countries, there are extra factors for the "First World".

Surprisingly, one source of food waste is labour shortage on farms. On average, about 7 per cent of American planted fields are not harvested each year – ranging between 2 per cent for potatoes and 15 per cent for wheat.

Another factor is the shift from a rural farming life to an urban non-agricultural life. Maybe this is why we seem to be less confident about our food. We don't trust our noses anymore to tell us when food has gone bad. Since 1974, the average American has increased personal food wastage by 50 per cent.

On average, one in seven truckloads of perishables delivered to supermarkets is thrown away. There are several reasons for this. Customers concentrate on appearance, so any "imperfect" (but perfectly edible) produce is culled. Much fresh produce arrives in pre-set quantities. Grapefruit may come in a case of 80, but if the grocer can sell only 50, then 30 are wasted.

At the consumer end, sometimes we let food rot in the pantry or fridge because we don't cook it in time. We might choose to eat in a restaurant, not at home, which creates other food wastage problems. In restaurants we order huge meals, and leave half uneaten. In some upmarket restaurants the kitchen cooks two identical meals for each customer – and then serves them the better-looking one, throwing away the perfectly fine, but less pretty, meal.

> We should cook only what we need – but if there is any left over, we can recycle it into that Prince of Foods, the Leftover.

Wastage happens in more downmarket restaurants as well. For example, in McDonald's the unsold chips have to be thrown out after 7 minutes, and the burgers after 20 minutes. About 10 per cent of all fast food is thrown out after it has been cooked.

In the US, wasted food makes up the single largest component of municipal solid waste. As a result, decomposing uneaten food leads to about one quarter of unintended methane emissions in the US. One organisation estimates that if "food scraps were removed from landfills [in the UK] . . . the level of greenhouse gas abatement would be equivalent to removing one-fifth of all the cars in the country from the road".

THE BIG FIX

The upside is that we can easily reduce food waste.

On the production side, if carrots are too "bent" or "curvy", they could be cut down to make "baby carrots". One farmer saw that 70 per cent of his carrots didn't get sold due to their irregular shape. After he cut the irregular ones down, he was able to sell them as baby carrots at US$0.50 per pound, as compared to US$0.17 per pound for regular-sized carrots.

As consumers, we can shop more wisely. We can buy fruit and vegetables even if they have tiny blemishes, and buy perishable foods in smaller portions. We can learn to recognise when food has actually gone bad, or if it's still edible. We need better standardisation and clarification of the Use-By Date labels on food, so that we don't throw out perfectly good food. We should cook only what we need – but if there is any left over, we can recycle it into that Prince of Foods, the Leftover.

The European Parliament has designated 2014 as the "European Year Against Food Waste", and has resolved to reduce food waste by 50 per cent by 2020. The path that food takes from the farm to the fork has many inefficient steps, so we can make a big improvement with relatively little effort – and we need to.

By the year 2050 the world's population will be about 9 billion people. If we want to feed everybody but we keep on wasting food at the same level as we do today, we will have to produce 70 per cent more food. So if we stop squandering our food, our job will be much easier.

This brings to mind the wonderful quote that has been attributed to (amongst others) Mahatma Ghandi: "Live simply so that others may simply live." Or, as your parents probably used to say, "Waste not, want not."

It's paradoxical that we in the Western World can control neither our Food Waste, nor our Waists . . .

Poor, Poor Pitiful Me

At one stage in my career, I was desperately poor. I had given up my well-paying job in New Guinea teaching and doing research into hair and wool, and had come to Sydney to make my fortune as an "underground film maker". There wasn't a lot of money in it, and I was living off my minuscule savings.

I soon discovered that the local greengrocers would get their new fruit and vegetable shipments on Monday mornings, at around 3 a.m. So, armed with a wheelbarrow, my housemates and I would arrive there around 2 a.m.

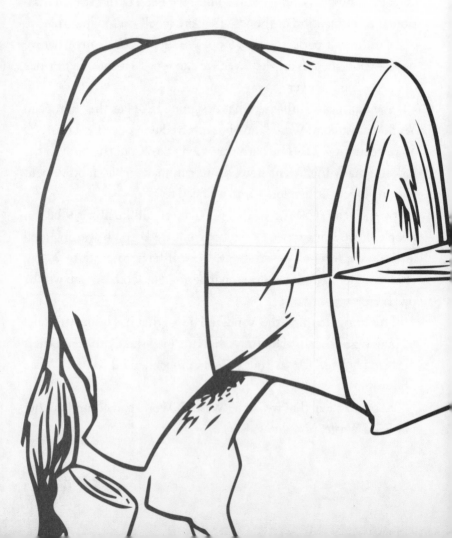

The greengrocers were perfectly happy for us to take away the boxes of last week's fruit and veg – that meant less rubbish for them to throw out. Most of it was spoiled, and went into the compost. But there was lots of unspoiled fruit and veg left over. We combined this with 20 kilogram bags of brown rice and soyabeans and ate very well indeed, for a very low cost.

I guess I was a trendsetter for Dumpster Diving, decades before it became popular.

31

WEIGHT-LOSS SURGERY

The Obesity Epidemic has well and truly hit Australia, with some five million people not just overweight, but actually obese. Even the Rich and Famous are getting fat. The difference for the wealthy is that some of them have weight-loss surgery and then suddenly reappear in public with a remarkably slimmed body. Politicians such as Joe Hockey, as well as the billionaire James Packer, have had dramatic transformations to their body shapes. Their experiences are stimulating interest in new versions of what used to be called Stomach Stapling.

You would, perfectly reasonably, think that Weight-loss Surgery worked simply by massively restricting how much food a person could cram into their stomach. But it turns out that it's much more complicated than that.

Imagine if Weight-loss Surgery made a peach suddenly taste like a fish.

WEIGHT-LOSS SURGERY 101

There are a few different types of Weight-loss Surgery. They all have the aim of making your stomach smaller in volume.

In some cases, Roux-en-Y surgery can cause inability to concentrate, difficulty in finding the right word and short-term memory problems.

Lap Banding is one type of operation. It involves placing a band around the stomach. The band can be adjusted to change the stomach volume, or it can be removed altogether. In Australia between 1994 and 2011, over 3000 patients had Lap Band Surgery. The average patient age was 47, and 78 per cent were women. In one Australian study, about one quarter of the patients had maintained a weight loss of 26 kilograms after 10 years. Interestingly, Lap Banding is not popular in the USA.

The other options involve actually cutting the stomach. There are a few different procedures used.

One operation is called the Vertical Sleeve Gastrectomy. This involves cutting away the majority of the stomach, leaving you a new smaller stomach in the shape of a long, narrow tube.

The Roux-en-Y, or Stomach Bypass, is a more invasive surgery. This involves stapling the stomach and then leaving only a very small pouch at the top. This pouch is then connected to the small intestine. With this operation, most of the stomach and part of the small intestine is bypassed.

After this surgery, most people lose their excess weight within 18 months. And over half of all the people who had Roux-en-Y operations kept their weight off.

Side Effects of Surgery

Weight-loss Surgery is certainly not an "easy" option.

Side effects include osteoporosis and metabolic bone disease, anaemia, loss of muscle mass, deficiencies of Vitamins D and B12, constipation and the risk of gallstones. There is also Gastric Reflux, as well as the embarrassing "Dumping Syndrome" where a small meal can give you nausea and vomiting. Very rarely people die as a result of complications of the surgery, such as Julienne McKay-Hall, aged 46, who had Weight-loss Surgery in November 2007 in Perth.

In some cases, Roux-en-Y surgery can cause inability to concentrate, difficulty in finding the right word and short-term memory problems. Anxiety and auditory hallucinations sometimes result.

The flipside is that other people report the exact opposite. After about three months, they report a "mental clarity".

WHY DOES SURGERY WORK?

The aim of all of these surgical operations is to prevent the stomach from expanding – so you can eat only a tiny amount. The result is that you feel full immediately, so you have no desire to eat.

(Some patients get around the smaller volume of the stomach by drinking high-calorie foods, such as liquid chocolate, to keep their energy intake high. Mind you, many patients lose the desire for high-calorie foods.)

You could reasonably assume that Early Fullness is the reason the surgery leads to weight loss.

But it turns out that there are at least two other reasons for the post-operative weight loss – changes in your brain and changes in your gut.

BRAIN CHANGE – PART 1

One patient reported that a glass of her favourite peach iced tea tasted like fish after her operation. She also found that raspberry tea tasted like fish.

There are many cases of patients who, immediately after the surgery, actually find the smell of sugar or fat quite repulsive. This is a complete turnaround.

One study used MRI scanners to examine the brains of patients both before and after Roux-en-Y surgery. The researchers showed the patients pictures of hamburgers or cakes. Before the surgery, the images of their favourite treats lit up the Reward Centres in their brains in joy and anticipation. After the surgery – nothing. Suddenly, their brains didn't respond to high-energy foods.

Lab rats that had Roux-en-Y surgery made more healthy choices post-surgery, without any prompting from a dietician. The rats immediately switched to foods that were lower in both fats and sugars.

Dr Stephen Benoit from the University of Cincinnati in Ohio is a Behavioural Neuroscientist who specialises in obesity. He said to *New Scientist*, "People who have lost weight after surgery don't report a compensatory increase in food cravings or hunger the way dieting people do."

Why did the food choices change so suddenly, and why did the food taste different?

BRAIN CHANGE – PART 2

The answer might be the so-called Brain-of-the-Gut. Yes, you do have a kind of "sub-Brain" in your gut. It's the Enteric Nervous System, which makes hormones that directly affect the Brain-in-Your-Skull.

When you think about it, it takes a lot of thought power to eat. You have to chew the food, mix it up and move it along the 10-metre length of the gut at various precise speeds. Every now and then, the food has to remain in one location for a while to allow further digestion. You also have to synchronise the addition of various juices and the release of hormones. And let's not forget the final stage – "expulsion" of the food.

> The Brain-in-Your-Skull makes a tiny 5 per cent of all the serotonin in your body.

If the Enteric Nervous System has to do all of this, it seems a little underpowered. It has only about half a million neurons – about 170,000 times fewer than the 85 to 100 billion neurons in your regular Brain. But while the Brain makes some 100 neurotransmitters, the Enteric Nervous System makes a respectable 40 neurotransmitters. That's a lot.

In fact, 95 per cent of serotonin, the so-called "feel-good" hormone, gets made by the Enteric Nervous System. In contrast, the Brain-in-Your-Skull makes a tiny 5 per cent of all the serotonin in your body.

Dopamine is another hormone. It's associated with the Pleasure and Reward System, and a bunch of other stuff. Your Brain makes 50 per cent of your total circulating supply, while your Enteric Nervous System makes the other 50 per cent.

So, your Enteric Nervous System makes "feel-good" hormones, and a variety of other hormones. These other hormones can make you hungry (for example, Ghrelin) or full (Glucagon-like Peptide-1, Peptide YY and Leptin).

GUT CHANGE

Another factor that helps weight loss after surgery seems to be that (somehow) the surgery changes the ratio of different micro-organisms in the gut. This new balance helps make the patient lose weight.

We have recently discovered that some 90 per cent of the cells in your body are invaders – bacteria and the like. (For more information, see my book *Brain Food*.) They live mostly in your gut. If you transplant micro-organisms between fat and skinny mice, the fat mice become skinny and the skinny mice get fat.

Dr Lee Kaplan and colleagues from Massachusetts General Hospital performed Roux-en-Y gastric bypass surgery on mice. They had two control groups – mice who had sham surgery and a regular diet, and mice who had sham surgery and a low-calorie diet. (Sham surgery is when you give the anaesthetic and open up the gut – but don't do the actual gut surgery.) They found that only the Roux-en-Y mice had major changes in the bacteria that lived in their gut.

The researchers next shifted these bacteria into lean, bacteria-free mice. The mice lost weight and fat. For comparison, the researchers then transplanted bacteria from the two control groups of mice into other lean, bacteria-free mice. This time, the bacteria-free mice did not lose weight.

Conclusion? Somehow, the Roux-en-Y surgery altered the types of bacteria in the gut of mice and this made them lose weight.

Does this happen to humans having Roux-en-Y surgery? At this stage, we just don't know.

Would it be possible to get the benefits without having the expensive and slightly risky surgery, by transplanting the bacteria? Again, we don't know – yet. How great would it be if you could get the results without the surgery?

WEIGHING IT ALL UP

Weight-loss Surgery is not as straightforward as it first seems.

It does have risks and complications, but the surgery can help weight reduction. Weight loss can lead to improvements in diabetes, sleep apnoea and high blood pressure. In the USA, where 36 per cent of people are obese, some 200,000 people get some kind of Weight-loss Surgery each year.

So, at the very least, Weight-loss Surgery is a key to a gut-wrenching experience . . .

32

WRINKLED SKIN IN THE BATH

Have you ever wished that you got out of the bath before your fingers and toes wrinkled like prunes? And have you ever wondered why they do wrinkle? Isn't skin supposed to be waterproof?

The answer I've used for a few decades to explain Why This Is So is, unfortunately, incorrect.

INCORRECT ANSWER

Why the wrinkling? The standard explanation is that your skin gets waterlogged and swells.

The wrinkling happens on the so-called "work areas" of the skin, where you interact with the Outside World. You grab stuff with your fingers, you walk on your feet and toes, and as a result you build up layers of protective dead skin on your hands and feet. This dead skin is rich in keratin, and this keratin is supposedly arranged in a kind of open mesh.

Go for a long swim, or soak in a bath, and the keratin that you've built up on your fingers and toes absorbs water, swells up . . . *voilà*, you now have wrinkled fingers and toes. The technical name for this is Aquatic Wrinkling.

Sounds reasonable – after all, the wrinkling doesn't seem to happen on "non-work areas" of your skin, such as your belly.

But here are a few problems with this explanation.

First, when your fingers and toes get all wrinkled, they shrink in volume, not expand. That means that this "open mesh keratin" shrank when it allegedly absorbed water, not expanded. Whoops! This seems 100 per cent illogical.

Second, a strange fact has been known since 1936. If you cut the Sympathetic Nerves to the fingers or toes, you can soak in water all day but you won't get any Aquatic Wrinkling of the fingers or toes. It turns out that this fact has been used to test nerve function since, you guessed it, 1936.

And third, beginning in the year 2003, Dr Einar Wilder-Smith from the National University of Singapore wrote a series of papers that pretty well demolished the old "it's-the-dead-skin-on-your-fingers-absorbing-water-and-swelling-and-making-wrinkles" explanation.

Wrinkling and Disease

It's not just diseases of the Sympathetic Nervous System that can reduce skin wrinkling in water.

It's also been observed in Diabetic Neuropathy, Parkinson's Disease and Leprosy (Hansen's Disease).

FIRST, SOME ANATOMY

To understand what's going on, you need to know a little anatomy.

First, the skin of your fingers and toes has one of the highest densities of sweat glands anywhere on your skin. (This turns out to be part of the reason why the most wrinkling happens on your fingers and toes.)

Second, the skin of your fingers and toes is indeed a work area. The outer layers of the skin sit on the inner layers like sheets of corrugated iron, so that when you grab something, the different layers don't slip over each other. In fact, not only are they corrugated, but the upper and lower layers are also tethered to each other at intervals of about a millimetre.

And third, there are special organs in your fingers and toes called Glomus Bodies, which are involved in both sensing temperature and regulating it. (They are also called Hoyer-Grosser's Organs.) A typical Glomus Body is about 0.25 to 0.5 millimetres across, and communicates with the rest of the Nervous System mostly via Sympathetic Nerves. Inside a Glomus Body, an artery runs directly into a vein. If Glomus Bodies let the warm blood run directly from the artery into the vein, the warm blood heads back to the heart, bypassing the fingertip – and the fingertip cools down. But if they don't let the warm blood take a shortcut, and instead force it to perfuse through the fingertip, then the fingertip warms up.

Sympathetic Nerves?

In medical school, we were taught that the Sympathetic Nervous System deals with emergencies.

In an emergency (like, say, being chased by a killer bunny rabbit), the Sympathetic Nervous System coordinates a whole bunch of activities. The blood supply to your skin reduces dramatically – so if you get cut, you won't bleed as much. The blood supply to your muscles is increased, so you can fight and run better. Your adrenal glands release adrenaline. Your pupils open up, to allow lots of light in. And so on.

As medical students, we were given a mnemonic as a memory aid. We were told that the Sympathetic Nervous System is involved in the Four Fs – Fight, Fright, Flight and "Making Love" . . .

PROBABLY CORRECT – 5 STEPS

So here are the five steps of Dr Wilder-Smith's theory. It's still a theory in the sense that not all – but most – of the steps have been proven or observed.

First, thanks to the huge number of sweat glands, water easily permeates into the skin of the fingers and toes. Sweat can normally flow out, and when you're soaking a little water can flow into the sweat glands.

Second, this incoming water locally dilutes the normally tightly regulated levels of salts in the skin.

Third, these diluted levels decrease the stability of the cell membranes in the local tissues. This leads to increased firing rates of the dense networks of Sympathetic Nerve fibres. These Sympathetic

Nerves help control the diameter of the blood vessels in the fingers and toes. When they fire, they close down these blood vessels – both the regular blood vessels and those in the Glomus Bodies.

Fourth, now that the blood vessels in the fingers and toes are partially closed down, the volume of the fingers and toes shrinks.

Fifth and finally, this shrinking is uneven and irregular due to the roughly 1 millimetre spacing of the "tethering" of the different skin layers. And that's how you get Aquatic Wrinkling.

EVOLUTION WINS AGAIN

What would be the evolutionary advantage of having your fingers and toes wrinkle when they soak in water?

Think about racing tyres. Dry Weather racing tyres have no tread at all – they are completely smooth to maximise grip. But Wet Weather racing tyres have grooves – to maximise grip in wet conditions. And, indeed, experiments with people gripping variously sized marbles and lead weights underwater show that the grip is significantly improved when the fingertips are wrinkled.

So I would like to apologise for accidentally misleading people for the past few decades, when the real explanation was right there at my fingertips the whole time . . .

ACKNOWLEDGMENTS

I would first like to thank all the Real Scientists and Mathematicians who were kind enough to look at my stories involving their Work or Field of Knowledge – and then to try clear up my errors and misinterpretations.

This list includes Professor Geraint Lewis (who tried manfully to correct my many misconceptions about Dark Energy, Dark Matter, Milky Way Collisions and Is Earth Losing Weight?), Adam Spencer (Cicadas in Their Prime), Professor Coby Schal (Cockroaches' Bittersweet Revenge), Professor Brian Schmidt (Nobel Laureate for Dark Energy) who is horrendously busy and wisely did not look at my story but is still a "good bloke" and whom I admire even more for having the sense to say "no" when necessary, Professor Jim Schirillo (About Face . . . Attractiveness), Emily Staub (Guinea Worm), Professor Andrew Przyblski (Phoney Relationships), Professor Ove Hoegh-Guldberg (Ocean Acidification), Professor

John Kheir (Oxygen Injection: Breath of Life), Richard Saunders of Australian Skeptics (Power Balance Bracelets), and Professor Einar Wilder-Smith (Wrinkled Skin in the Bath).

And of course, if any errors remain after their advice, the fault is entirely mine.

Thanks also to the readers of first drafts and punchline writers, Mary Dobbie, Alice and Lola Kruszelnicki, Sophie Hamley, Caroline Pegram and my ABC producers Dan Driscoll, David Moore, Tim Brunero and Daniel Glover.

The People from Pan were wonderful, inspiring and, luckily, forgiving. Claire Craig published beautifully, Emma Rafferty and the still-mysterious Sarah J.H. Fletcher edited (an entirely different but essential skill to writing), while Douglas Holgate pencilled lovely illustrations. Jon MacDonald and the team from Xou Creative laid out the book, making it look very handsome. But a book must fly from the shelf into the hands of the Dear Reader. So Jace Armstrong designed the Publicity Campaign while Charlotte Ree went on the road and made it happen.

Like Big Science, this book was a Big Team Effort.

REFERENCES

1. 3D Printing

"Print Me a Heart and a Set of Arteries", by Peter Aldhous, *New Scientist*, 13 April 2006, No. 2547, page 19.

"Case History: A Factory on Your Desk", by Todd May, *The Economist: Technology Quarterly*, 3 September 2009.

"Print Me a Stradivarius", *The Economist*, 10 February 2011.

"Make Your Own Drugs with a 3D Printer", by Katharine Sanderson, *New Scientist*, 17 April 2012, No. 2861, pages 8–9.

"Building Research Equipment with Free, Open-Source Hardware", by Joshua M. Pearce, *Science*, 14 September 2012, Vol. 337, No. 6100, pages 1303–1304.

"Additive Manufacturing: GE, the World's Largest Manufacturer, Is on the Verge of Using 3-D Printing to Make Jet Parts", by Martin LaMonica, 23 April 2013, http://www.technologyreview.com/featuredstory/513716/additive-manufacturing/

"To Print the Impossible: Will 3-D Printing Transform Conventional Manufacturing?", by Larry Greenemeier, *Scientific American*, 7 May 2013, pages 30–33.

"3D-Printed Gun's First Shots Spark Calls for Ban", by Jacob Aron, *New Scientist*, No. 2916, 7 May 2013.

"3D Print – In Space", *New Scientist*, 11 May 2013, No. 2916, page 7.

"NASA Asks: Could 3D Printed Food Fuel a Mission to Mars", by Amrita Jayakumar, *The Washington Post*, 21 May 2013.

"Bioresorbable Airway Splint Created with a Three-Dimensional Printer", by David A. Zopf et al., *New England Journal of Medicine*, 23 May 2013, Vol. 368, pages 2043–2045.

2. A Buzz About Honeybee Stings

"Removing Bee Stings", by P. Kirk Visscher et al., *The Lancet*, 3 August 1996, Vol. 348, No. 9023, pages 301–302.

"Minding Their Own Beeswax", by Forrest Wickman, *Slate*, 19 June 2012, http://www.slate.com/articles/health_and_science/explainer/2012/06/busy_as_a_bee_are_bees_really_busy_.html

"Egg-Laying Worker Bees", by Khalil Hamdan, http://www.jordanbru.info/Egg.htm

3. About Face . . . Attractiveness

"Turning the Other Cheek: Profile Direction in Self-Portraiture", by Richard Latto, *Journal of the International Association of Empirical Aesthetics*, 1996, Vol. 14, No. 1, pages 89–98.

"Emotive Hemispheric Difference Measured in Real-Life Portraits using Pupil Diameter and Subjective Aesthetic Preferences", by Kelsey Blackburn and James Schirillo, *Experimental Brain Research*, June 2012, Vol. 219, No. 4, pages 447–455.

4. Alcohol and Artificial Sweeteners

"Artificially Sweetened Versus Regular Mixers Increase Gastric Emptying and Alcohol Absorption", by Keng-Liang Wu et al., *The American Journal of Medicine*, September 2006, Vol. 119, No. 9, pages 802–804.

"Artificial Sweeteners Versus Regular Mixers Increase Breath Alcohol Concentrations in Male and Female Social Drinkers", by Cecile A. Marczinski and Amt L. Stamates, *Alcoholism: Clinical and Experimental Research*, 6 December 2012, pages 1–7.

5. Biorythms: A New Equation

"The Biorhythm Principle: A Crucial Factor in Well-Being and Human Relations", by Brian Krauze-Poray, *Nexus*, June–July 1992, Vol. 2, No. 8, pages 21–24.

The Skeptic's Dictionary: A Collection of Strange Beliefs, Amusing Deceptions, and Dangerous Delusions, by Robert Todd Carroll, 2003, John Wiley and Sons, Inc, Hoboken, pages 58–62.

"Does 'Spring Fever' Exist?", by Christie Nicholson, *Scientific American*, April 2008, Vol. 298, No. 116, April 2008, page 115.

6. Blood–Brain Barrier

"Breaking Down Barriers" by Greg Miller, *Science*, 16 August 2002, Vol. 297, No. 5584, pages 1116–1118.

"The Blood–Brain Barrier: An Overview. Structure, Regulation and Clinical Implications", by Praveen Ballabh et al., *Neurobiology of Disease*, June 2004, Vol. 16, No. 1, pages 1–13.

"Breaching the Barrier", by Alan Dove, *Nature Biotechnology*, November 2008, Vol. 26, No. 11, pages 1213–1215.

"Meningococcal Type IV Pili Recruit the Polarity Complex to Cross the Brain Endothelium", by Mathieu Coureuil et al., *Science*, 3 July 2009, Vol. 325, No. 5936, pages 83–87.

"The Blood–Brain Barrier", by Alan M. Palmer, *Neurobiology of Disease*, January 2010, Vol. 37, No. 1, pages 1–2.

"The Role of the Blood–CNS Barrier in CNS Disorders and Their Treatment", by Alan M. Palmer, *Neurobiology of Disease*, January 2010, Vol. 37, No. 1, pages 3–12.

"Structure and Function of the Blood–Brain Barrier", by N. Joan Abbott et al., *Neurobiology of Disease*, January 2010, Vol. 37, No. 1, pages 13–25.

"The Blood–Brain Barrier and Immune Function and Dysfunction", by William A. Banks and Michelle A. Erickson, *Neurobiology of Disease*, January 2010, Vol. 37, No. 1, pages 26–32.

"Assessment of the Blood–Brain Barrier in CNS Drug Discovery", by Phil Jeffrey and Scott Summerfield, *Neurobiology of Disease*, January 2010, Vol. 37, No. 1, pages 33–37.

"Measurement of the Pharmacokinetics and Pharmacodynamics of Neuroactive Compounds", by Mohammad S. Alavijeh and Alan M. Palmer, *Neurobiology of Disease*, January 2010, Vol. 37, No. 1, pages 38–47.

"Approaches to Transport Therapeutic Drugs Across the Blood–Brain Barrier to Treat Brain Diseases", by Reinhard Gabathuler, *Neurobiology of Disease*, January 2010, Vol. 37, No. 1, pages 48–57.

"Looking at The Blood–Brain Barrier: Molecular Anatomy and Possible Investigation Approaches", by Filipa Lourenço Cardoso et al., *Brain Research Reviews*, 24 September 2010, Vol. 64, No. 2, pages 328–363.

"Maybe You Do Need a Hole in Your Head – To Let the Medicine In", by Carl Zimmer, *Discover*, November 2011, pages 32–33.

"Breaking the Brain Barrier", by Jeneen Interlandi, *Scientific American*, June 2013, Vol 308, No. 6, pages 44–49.

7. Cicadas in Their Prime

"The Cicada. A Harbinger of Summer", by H.I.W., *The Sydney Morning Herald*, 21 January 1928, page 21.

"Cicadas Shows Up after a Prime Number of Years", by Mario Markus and Eric Goles, *Mathematical Intelligencer*, Spring 2002, Vol. 24, No. 2, pages 30–32.

"The Orgy in Your Backyard", by Jeffrey A. Lockwood, *The New York Times*, 20 May 2004.

"Flying Insects Threaten to Deafen Japan", by David Cyranoski, *Nature*, 30 August 2007, Vol. 448, page 977.

"Independent Divergence of 13- and 17-year Life Cycles Among Three Periodical Cicada Lineages", by Teiji Sota et al., *Proceedings of the National Academy of Sciences*, 23 April 2013, Vol. 110, No. 17, pages 6919–6924.

"17 Years to Hatch an Invasion", by Carl Zimmer, *The New York Times*, 14 May 2013.

8. Clueless

"On Being Sane in Insane Places", by D.L. Rosenhan, *Science*, 19 January 1973, Vol 179, No. 4070, pages 250–258.

"Unskilled and Unaware of It: How Difficulties in Recognizing One's Own Incompetence Lead to Inflated Self-Assessments", by Justin Kruger and David Dunning, *Journal of Personality and Social Psychology*, December 1999, Vol. 77, No. 6, pages 1121–1134.

"How Chronic Self-Views Influence (and Potentially Mislead) Estimates of Performance", by Joyce Ehrlinger and David Dunning, *Journal of Personality and Social Psychology*, January 2003, Vol. 84, No. 1, pages 5–17.

"Mind-Reading and Metacognition: Narcissism, Not Actual Competence, Predicts Self-Estimated Ability", by Daniel R. Ames and Lara K. Kammrath, *Journal of Nonverbal Behaviour*, August 2004, Vol. 28, No. 3, pages 187–209.

"Skilled or Unskilled, But Still Unaware of It: How Perceptions of Difficulty Drive Miscalibration in Relative Comparisons", by Katherine A. Burson et al., *Journal of Personality and Social Psychology*, January 2006, Vol. 90, No. 1, pages 60–77.

"The Anosognosic's Dilemma: Something's Wrong, But You'll Never Know What It Is", by Errol Morris, 24 June 2010, http://opinionator.blogs.nytimes.com/2010/06/20/the-anosognosics-dilemma-1/.

9. Cockroaches' Bittersweet Revenge

"Changes in Taste Neurons Support the Emergence of an Adaptive Behaviour in Cockroaches", by Ayako Wada-Katsumata et al., *Science*, 24 May 2013, Vol. 340, No. 6135, pages 972–975.

"The Roach's Secret", by Wendy Zuckerman, *New Scientist*, 16 April 2011, No. 2808, pages 40–42.

"Wily Cockroaches Find Another Survival Trick: Laying Off the Sweets", by James Gorman, *The New York Times*, 23 May 2013.

"A Mosquito That Won't Ruin a Barbecue", by Douglas Quenqua, *The New York Times*, 3 June 2013.

"*Orco* Mutant Mosquitoes Lose Strong Preference for Humans and Are Not Repelled by Volatile DEET", by Matthew DeGennaro et al., *Nature*, Vol. 498, 27 June 2013, pages 487–491.

10. Dark Energy

"Special Report: Revolution in Cosmology", *Scientific American*, January 1999, Vol. 280, No. 1, page 45.

"Surveying Space-Time with Supernovae", by Craig J. Hogan et al., *Scientific American*, January 1999, Vol. 280, No. 1, pages 46–52.

"Cosmological Antigravity", by Lawrence M. Krauss, *Scientific American*, January 1999, Vol. 280, No. 1, pages 53–59.

"Will Dark Energy Steal All the Stars?", by Steve Nadis, *Astronomy*, March 2003, Vol. 31, No. 3, pages 42–47.

"From Slowdown to Speedup", by Adam G. Reiss and Michael S. Turner, *Scientific American*, February 2004, Vol. 290, No. 4, pages 62–67.

"Where Is the Universe Heading?", by James S. Trefil, *Astronomy*, July 2006, Vol. 34, No. 7, pages 36–41.

"Will Dark Energy Tear the Universe Apart?", by Liz Kruesi, *Astronomy*, February 2009, Vol. 37, No. 2, pages 34–39.

"Is the Big Bang in Trouble?", by Daniel Pendick, *Astronomy*, April 2009, Vol. 37, No. 4, pages 48–51.

"Confronting the Dark", by Zeeya Merali, *Discover*, May 2013, Vol. 34, No. 4, pages 38–47.

"Chasing Shadows", by Stephen Battersby, *New Scientist*, 11 May 2013, Vol. 218, No. 2916, pages 32–35.

11. Dark Matter

"Astronomers Discover First 'Microlens'", by Nigel Henbest, *New Scientist*, Vol. 1675, No. 1675, 29 July 1989, pp 35–39.

"Dark Matter in Spiral Galaxies", by Vera C. Rubin, *Scientific American*, Vol. 248, June 1983, pages 88–101.

"Detection of Hot Gas in the Filament Connecting the Clusters of Galaxies Abell 222 and Abell 223", by Norbert Werner et al., *Astronomy and Astrophysics Letters*, May 2008, Vol. 482, L29–L33.

"Near-infrared Background Anisotropies from Diffuse Intrahalo Light of Galaxies", by Asantha Cooray et al., *Nature*, Vol. 490, 25 October 2012, pages 514–516.

12. Drinking Glass Shapes Perception

"Glass Shape 'Affects Drink Size'", *BBC News*, 23 December 2005, http://news.bbc.co.uk/2/hi/health/4552668.stm.

"Shape of Glass and Amount of Alcohol Poured: Comparative Study of Effect of Practice and Concentration", by Brian Wansink et al., *British Medical Journal*, 24 December 2005, Vol. 331, No. 7531, pages 1512–1514.

"Glass Shape Influences Consumption Rate for Alcoholic Beverages", by Angela S. Attwood et al., *PLOS One*, August 2012, Vol. 7, No. 8, e43007, pages 1–6.

"Beware the Beer-Shaped Curve", by Emily Underwood, *Australian Financial Review*, 12 October 2012, page 8.

13. DVD ©opyright Theft

"Copyright Corruption Scandal Surrounds Anti-Piracy Campaign", 1 December 2011, http://torrentfreak.com/copyright-corruption-scandal-surrounds-anti-piracy-campaign-111201/.

"How to End the Copyright Wars", by Jonathan Zittrain, *Nature*, 15 January 2009, Vol. 457, pages 264–265.

"Piracy Advert Used Stolen Music", *Atomic*, August 2012, page 7.

14. Eight Glasses of Water Per Day

"Neurogenic Disorders of Osmoregulation", by G.L. Robertson et al., *American Journal of Medicine*, February 1982, Vol. 72, No. 2, pages 339–353.

Your Body's Many Cries for Water, by Fereydoon Batmanghelidj, 3rd edition, Global Health Solutions, Falls Church, 2008.

"'Drink At Least 8 Glasses of Water a Day.' Really? Is There Scientific Evidence for 8×8?", by Heinz Valtin, *American Journal of Physiology – Regulatory, Integrative and Comparative Physiology*, November 2002, Vol. 283, No. 5, pages R993–R1004.

"Water, Water Everywhere", by Rosemary Stanton, *Australian Doctor*, 11 December 2009, pages 39–40.

15. Food Portion Size

"Portion Size of Food Affects Energy Intake in Normal-Weight and Overweight Men and Women", by Barbara J. Rolls et al., *The American Journal of Clinical Nutrition*, December 2002, Vol. 76, No. 6, pages 1207–1213.

"Effects on Hunger and Satiety, Perceived Portion Size and Pleasantness of Taste of Varying the Portion Size of Foods: A Brief Review of Selected Studies", by Tanja V.E. Kral, *Appetite*, January 2006, Vol. 46, No. 1, pages 103–105.

"The Portion Size Effect: A Review", by Vincent Brienza et al., *Journal of Undergraduate Life Sciences*, June 2010, Vol. 4, No. 1, pages 78–80.

16. Free Will

"Does Free Will Arise Freely?", by Michael Pauen, *Scientific American Mind*, January 2004, pages 40–47.

"Unconscious Determinants of Free Decisions in the Human Brain", by Chun Siong Soon et al., *Nature Neuroscience*, May 2009, Vol. 11, No. 5, pages 543–545.

"Nature Versus Nurture: A Moral Mind Field", by Roger Scruton, *The Australian Financial Review*, 24 February 2012.

"Predicting Free Choices for Abstract Intentions", by Chun Siong Soon et al., *Proceedings of the National Academy of Sciences*, 9 April 2013, Vol. 110, No. 15, pages 6217–6222.

"Beyond the Brain", by David Brooks, *The New York Times*, 17 June 2013.

17. Functional Food

"Scale and Causes of Lead Contamination in Chinese Tea", by Wen-Yan Han et al., *Environmental Pollution*, January 2006, Vol. 139, No. 1, pages 125–132.

"Foods with Benefits, or So They Say", by Natasha Singer, *The New York Times*, 14 May 2011.

"Reality Check: There is No Such Thing as a Miracle Food", by Maki Inoue-Choi et al., *Nutrition and Cancer*, 26 February 2013, Vol. 65, No. 2, pages 165–168.

"Does Green Mean Healthy? Nutrition Label Color Affects Perceptions of Healthfulness", by Jonathon P. Schuldt, *Health Communication*, 27 February 2013, DOI: 10.1080/10410236.2012.725270.

"What's in Your Green Tea", by Anahad O'Connor, The New York Times, 23 May 2013.

"A Bad Wrap", by Kelsey Castanon, Shape, July–August 2013, page 100.

18. Guinea Worm

"Sudan's War and Eradication of Dracunculiasis" by Donald R. Hopkins and P. Craig Withers, Jr., *The Lancet*, 1 December 2002, Vol. 360, pages s21–s22.

"Dose of Tenacity Wears Down a Horrific Disease" by Donald G. McNeil Jr., *The New York Times*, 26 March 2006.

"The Guinea Worm: A Fond Obituary", by Carl Zimmer, *National Geographic: The Loom* blog, 21 January 2013, http://phenomena.nationalgeographic.com/2013/01/24/the-guinea-worm-a-fond-obituary/.

19. High-pitched Hot Chocolate

"On the Note Emitted from a Mug when Mixing Instant Coffee", by W.E. Farrell et al., *Mathematical Proceedings of the Cambridge Philosophical Society*, January 1969, Vol. 65, No. 1, pages 365–367.

"The Hot Chocolate Effect", by Frank S. Crawford, *American Journal of Physics*, May 1982, Vol. 50, No. 5, pages 398–404.

20. Hoverboard

http://en.wikipedia.org/wiki/GSh-6-30

http://en.wikipedia.org/wiki/GAU-8_Avenger

http://en.wikipedia.org/wiki/Fairchild_Republic_A-10_Thunderbolt_II

"Machine Gun Jetpack", by Randall Monroe, http://what-if.xkcd.com/21/

21. Is Earth Losing Weight?

"Earth's Energy Imbalance: Confirmation and Implications", by James Hansen et al., *Science*, 3 June 2005, Vol. 308, No. 5727, pages 1431–1435.

"The Planetary Air Leak", by David C. Catling et al., *Scientific American*, May 2009, Vol. 300, pages 24–31.

"Who, What, Why: Is the Earth Getting Lighter?", by Charlotte McDonald, *BBC News*, 31 January 2012, http://www.bbc.co.uk/news/magazine-16787636.

"Loss in Earth Mass Due to Extraterrestrial Space Exploration Missions", by Shivam Saxena and Mahesh Chandra, *International Journal of Scientific and Research Publications*, May 2013, Vol. 3, No. 5, www.ijsrp.org.

22. Milky Way Collisions

"The Final Plunge", by Mark Morris, *Nature*, 5 January 2012, Vol. 481, pages 32–33.

"A Gas Cloud on Its Way towards the Supermassive Black Hole at the Centre of the Galaxy", by S. Gillessen et al., *Nature*, 5 January 2012, Vol. 481, pages 51–54.

"The New Milky Way", by Ann Finkbeiner, *Nature*, 4 October 2012, Vol. 490, pages 24–27.

"Decade of the Monster", by Ron Cowen, *Science*, 29 March 2013, Vol. 339, No. 6127, pages 1514–1516.

"Close Approach to Galactic Centre of Cloud G2 in July 2013", by Paul LaViolette, *Nexus*, Vol. 20, No. 3, April–May 2013, pages 51–54.

"This Dust Cloud is About to Be Swallowed by the Black Hole at the Centre of Our Galaxy: What Will Happen Next?", by Paul Sutherland, *Focus*, June 2013, pages 36–41.

23. Money Magnets: The Science of Economics

"That's the Way the Money Goes", by Mark Buchanan, *New Scientist*, Vol. 167, No. 2252, 19 August 2000, pages 22–26.

"Wealth Condensation in a Simple Model of Economy", by Jean-Philippe Bouchaud

and Marc Mezard, *Physica A: Statistical Mechanics and Its Applications*, July 2000, Vol. 282, No. 3–4, pages 536–545, http://arxiv.org/abs/condmat/0002374.

"The Long Tail", by Chris Anderson, *Wired*, October 2004, pages 170–177.

"Tax Cuts Make Rich Americans Richer", by David Cay Johnston, *Australian Financial Review*, 7 April 2006, page 58.

"Econophysics: Culture Crash", by Philip Ball, *Nature*, 8 June 2006, Vol. 441, No. 7094, pages 686–688.

"Corporate Wealth Share Rises for Top-Income Americans", by David Cay Johnston, *The New York Times*, 29 June 2006.

"Bush Tax Cuts Offer Most for Very Rich, Study Finds", by Edmund L. Andrews, *The New York Times*, 8 January 2007.

"Inequalities in Premature Mortality in Britain: Observational Study from 1921 to 2007", by Bethan Thomas et al., *BMJ*, 2010;341:c3639

"The Spread of Inequality", by Deborah S. Rogers et al., *PLOS One*, September 2011, Vol. 6, No. 9, pages e24683.

"The Hard Core of Power", by Andy Coghlan and Debora MacKenzie, *New Scientist*, 22 October 2011, Vol. 212, No. 2835, pages 8–9.

"Poor Little Rich Minds: The Price of Wealth", by Michael Bond, *New Scientist*, 26 April 2012, Vol. 214, No. 2861, pages 52–54.

"The Price of Offshore Revisited" by James S. Henry, Tax Justice Network, July 2012, http://www.taxjustice.net/cms/front_content.php?idcat=148.

"The Age of Inequality", Special Report, New Scientist, 28 July 2012, Vol. 215, No. 2875, pages 37–45.

24. Ocean Acidification

"Actual and Anticipated Petrographic Effects of Carbonate Undersaturation in Shallow Seawater", by E.T. Alexandersson, *Nature*, 19 August 1976, Vol. 262, No. 5570, pages 653–657.

"Climate Change Could Stop Corals Fixing Themselves", by Devin Powell, *New Scientist*, 5 September 2008.

"Ocean Biogeochemistry: Calcification and CO_2", by Jean-Pierre Gattuso and Robert W. Buddemeier, *Nature*, 21 September 2000, Vol. 407, No. 6802, pages 311–313.

"Anthropogenic Ocean Acidification over the Twenty-First Century and Its Impact on Calcifying Organisms", by James C. Orr et al., *Nature*, 29 September 2005, Vol. 437, No. 7059, pages 681–686.

"Coral Reefs under Rapid Climate Change and Ocean Acidification", by O. Hoegh Guldberg et al., *Science*, 14 December 2007, Vol. 318, No. 5857, pages 1737–1742.

"Atmospheric CO_2 Stabilisation and Ocean Acidification", by Long Cao and Ken Caldeira, *Geophysical Research Letters*, October 2008, Vol. 35, No. 19, L19609.

"Pteropods in Southern Ocean Ecosystems", by B.P.V. Hunt et al., *Progress in Oceanography*, September 2008, Vol. 78, No. 3, pages 193–221.

"Ocean Acidification: Present Conditions and Future Changes in a High-CO_2 World" by Richard A. Feely et al., *Oceanography*, December 2009, Vol. 22, No. 4, pages 36–47.

"Oceans Acidifying at Unprecedented Speed", by Michael Marshall, *New Scientist*, 10 March 2012, Vol. 213, No. 2855, pages 4–5.

"The Pacific Oyster, *Crassostrea gigas*, Shows Negative Correlation to Naturally Elevated Carbon Dioxide Levels: Implications for Near-Term Ocean Acidification Impacts", by Alan Barton et al.. *Limnology and Oceanography*, May 2012, Vol. 57, No. 3, pages 698–710.

"Climate Change Offers Grim Long-Term Prognosis for Seafood: The Ocean Acidification Caused by Rising Levels of Carbon Dioxide in the Atmosphere will Disrupt Marine Ecosystems", by Lauren Lorello and ClimateWire, 28 September 2012, *Scientific American*, http://www.scientificamerican.com/article.cfm?id=climate-change-offers-grim-long-term-prognosis-for-seafood.

"Animals Are Already Dissolving in Southern Ocean Acid", by Michael Marshall, *New Scientist*, 25 November 2012.

"Extensive Dissolution of Live Pteropods in the Southern Ocean", by N. Bednaršek et al., *Nature Geoscience*, December 2012, Vol. 5, No. 12, pages 881–885.

"Reduced Calcification and Lack of Acclimatization by Coral Colonies Growing in Areas of Persistent Natural Acidification", by Elizabeth D. Crook et al., *Proceeding of the National Academy of Sciences of the United States of America*, 2 July 2013, Vol. 110, No. 27, pages 11044–11049.

25. Oxygen Injection: Breath of Life

"Supplemental Systemic Oxygen Support Using an Intestinal Intraluminal Membrane Oxygenator", by Brian D. Gross et al., *Artificial Organs*, November 2000, Vol. 24, No. 11, pages 864–869.

"Perfluorocarbon-Based Oxygen Carriers: Review of Products and Trials", by Camila Irene Castro and Juan Carlos Briceno, *Artificial Organs*, August 2010, Vol. 34, No. 8, pages 622–634.

"Boosting Oxygenation During Acute Respiratory Failure", by Raymond C. Koehler, *Science Translational Medicine*, 27 June 2012, Vol. 4, No. 140, pages 140fs21 1–2.

"Oxygen Gas-Filled Microparticles Provide Intravenous Oxygen Delivery", by John N. Kheir et al., *Science Translational Medicine*, 27 June 2012, Vol. 4, No. 140, pages 140ra88 1–10.

26. Pain Ray

"Thresholds of Microwave-Evoked Warmth Sensations in Human Skin", by Dennis W. Blick et al., *Bioelectromagnetics*, 1997, Vol. 18, No. 6, pages 403–409.

"Say Hello to the Goodbye Weapon", by David Hambling, *The New Yorker*, 5 December 2006.

"The Quest for the Nonkiller App", by Stephen Mihm, *The New York Times*, 25 July 2004.

"A World of Hurt", by David Hambling, *New Scientist*, 11 May 2013, pages 44–47.

27. Phoney Relationships

"Can You Connect Me Now? How the Presence of Mobile Communication Technology Influences Face-to-face Conversation Quality", by Andrew K. Przybylski and Netta Weinstein, *Journal of Social and Personal Relationships*, pages 1–10, 19 July 2012.

"How Your Cell Phone Hurts Your Relationships", by Helen Lee Lin, *Scientific American* Mind Matters blog, 4 September 2012, http://www.scientificamerican.com/article.cfm?id=how-your-cell-phone-hurts-your-relationships

28. Power Balance Bracelets

"Continuous Excitation of Planetary Free Oscillations by Atmospheric Disturbances", by Naoki Kobayashi and Kiwamu Nishida, *Nature*, 24 September 1998, Vol. 395, No. 6700, pages 357–360.

"Atmospheric Excitation of Planetary Free Oscillations", by Naoki Kobayashi and Kiwamu Nishida, *Journal of Physics: Condensed Matter*, Vol. 10, No. 49, 14 December 1998, pages 11557–11560.

"HAARP's Threat to the 'Voice Of The Planet'", by Richard Alan Miller and Iona Miller, *Nexus*, June–July 2003, Vol. 10, No. 3, pages 17–24.

"Siren Song of the Earth: Investigating Vortex Theory and EM Signals with Ben Lonetree", by Ben Lonetree and Iona Miller, *Nexus*, February–March 2005, Vol. 12, No. 2, pages 41–44.

"Free Energy from Tesla's Wireless Electricity", by Thomas Valone, *Nexus*, April 2005, Vol. 12, No. 3, pages 51–54.

"The Earth's "Hum" is Driven by Ocean Waves over the Continental Shelves", by Spahr C. Webb, *Nature*, 15 February 2007, Vol. 445, No. 7129, pages 754–756.

"Slap on the Wrist for Power Balance", by Mark Russell, *The Sydney Morning Herald*, 21 November 2010.

"Power Wristbands Banned and Refunds Ordered by ACCC", by Nathan Mawby, *The Herald Sun* (Melbourne), 23 December 2010.

"Facts and Fiction of the Schumann Resonance", by Brian Dunning, *Skeptoid* Podcast, Episode 352, 5 March 2013, http://skeptoid.com/episodes/4532.

29. Psychopath Wisdom

"Crime Profiles and Conditional Release Performance of Psychopathic and Non-Psychopathic Sexual Offenders", by Stephen Porter et al., *Legal And Criminological Proceedings*, February, 2009, Vol. 14, pages 109–118.

"Into the Mind of a Killer", by Alison Abbott, *Nature*, 15 March 2001, Vol. 410, No. 6826, pages 296–298.

"Violence Viewed by Psychopathic Murderers", by Nicola S. Gray et al., *Nature*, 29 May 2003, Vol. 423, No. 6939, pages 497–498.

"Fearless Dominance and the US Presidency: Implications of Psychopathic Traits for Successful and Unsuccessful Political Leadership", by Scott O. Lilienfeld et al., *Journal of Personality and Social Psychology*, September 2012, Vol. 103, No. 3, pages 498–505.

"The Wisdom of Psychopaths", by Kevin Dutton, *Scientific American*, 12 October 2012, Vol. 307, pages 68–71.

"Olfactory Abilities and Psychopathy: Higher Psychopathy Scores Are Associated with Poorer Odor Discrimination and Identification", by Mehmet K. Mahmut and Richard J. Stevenson, *Chemical Perception*, December 2012, Vol. 5, No. 3–4, pages 300–307.

30. Wasted Food – From Farm to Fork to Landfill

American Wasteland: How America Throws Away Nearly Half of Its Food (and What We Can Do About It), by Jonathan Bloom, Da Capo Lifelong Books, Boston, 2010.

"More Food, Less Energy", by Michael E. Webber, *Scientific American*, January 2012, Vol. 306, pages 62–67.

"Wasted: How America Is Losing Up to 40 Percent of its Food From Farm to Fork to Landfill", by Dana Gunders, *Natural Resources Defense Council*, NRDC Issue Paper, New York, August 2012, IP:12-06-B, http://www.nrdc.org/food/files/wasted-food-ip.pdf.

"US Falls Behind in Global Drive to Stop Billions of Dollars in Food Waste", by Dina Elboghdady, *The Sydney Morning Herald*, 23 August 2012, page 9.

"Global Food: Waste Not, Want Not", by Tim Cox, Institution of Mechanical Engineers, London, January 2013, http://www.imeche.org/docs/default-source/reports/Global_Food_Report.pdf?sfvrsn=0.

31. Weight-loss Surgery

"Change Your Stomach, Change Your Brain", by Samantha Murphy, *New Scientist*, 23 May 2012, No. 2865, pages 42–45.

"Risks Come with the Incredible Shrinking Process", by Dominic White, *The Australian Financial Review*, 18 January 2013.

"Conserved Shifts in the Gut Microbiota Due to Gastric Bypass Reduce Host Weight and Adiposity", by Alice. P. Liou et al., *Science Translational Medicine*, 27 March 2013, Vol. 5, Vol. 178 (41), pages 1–11.

32. Wrinkled Skin in the Bath (Wrong Again)

"Circulatory Changes in Fingers in Some Diseases of Nervous System with Special Reference to Digital Atrophy of Peripheral Nerve Lesions", by T. Lewis and G.W. Pickering, *Clinical Science*, 1936, Vol. 2, pages 149–175.

"Water-Immersion Wrinkling Is Due to Vasoconstriction", by Einar P.V. Wilder-Smith and Adeline Chow, *Muscle and Nerve*, March 2003, Vol. 27, No. 3, pages 307–311.

"Water Immersion Wrinkling: Physiology and Use as an Indicator of Sympathetic Function", by Einar P.V. Wilder-Smith, *Clinical Autonomic Research*, April 2004, Vol. 14, pages 125–131.

"Water Immersion and EMLA Cause Similar Digit Skin Wrinkling and Vasoconstriction", by Einar P.V. Wilder-Smith and Adeline Chow, *Microvascular Research*, July 2003, Vol. 66, No. 1, pages 68–72.

"Are Wet-Induced Wrinkled Fingers Primate Rain Treads?", by Mark Changizi et al., *Brain, Behaviour and Evolution*, 23 June 2011, Vol. 77, No. 4, pages 286–290.

"Really? The Claim: Fingers Wrinkle Because of Water Absorption", by Anahad O'Connor, http://well.blogs.nytimes.com/2011/09/12/really-the-claim-fingers-wrinkle-because-of-water-absorption/, 15 September 2011.

"Water-Induced Finger Wrinkles Improve Handling of Wet Objects", by Kyriacos Kareklas et al., *Biology Letters*, Vol. 9, 9 January 2013.

ALSO BY DR KARL KRUSZELNICKI . . .

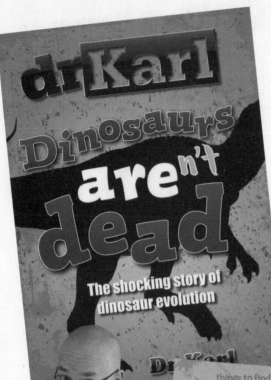

drKarl

Dinosaurs aren't dead

The shocking story of dinosaur evolution

Dr Karl Kruszelnicki

DR KARL'S

things to find • puzzles • word clues

mazes

mix & match

BIG BOOK OF

SCIENCE STUFF
and nonsense

things to draw

what am I?

odd one out

dot-to-dot

Dr Karl Kruszelnicki

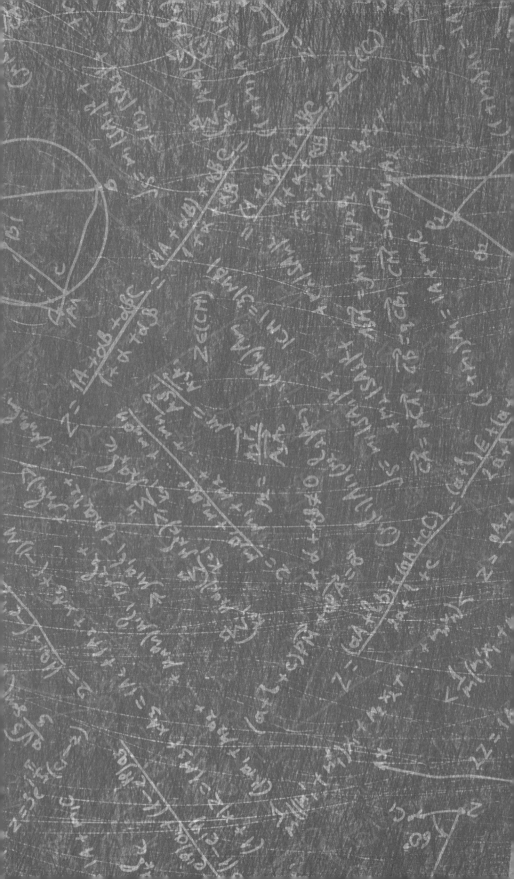